D0487684

THE SOLAR GRANULATION

THE INTERNATIONAL ASTROPHYSICS SERIES

VOLUME EIGHT

THE INTERNATIONAL ASTROPHYSICS SERIES

General Editors:

Sir Bernard Lovell, O.B.E., F.R.S.

Professor of Radio Astronomy
University of Manchester

Zdeněk Kopal

Professor of Astronomy
University of Manchester

THE SOLAR GRANULATION

R. J. Bray and R. E. Loughhead

Commonwealth Scientific and Industrial Research Organization
National Standards Laboratory, Sydney, Australia

VOLUME EIGHT
THE INTERNATIONAL ASTROPHYSICS SERIES

CHAPMAN AND HALL LTD.
11 NEW FETTER LANE, LONDON, E.C.4

First published 1967

Printed in Great Britain at the Alden Press, Oxford,
and bound by James Burn & Co Ltd

Distribution in the U.S.A.
by Barnes & Noble, Inc

Editors' Note

The aim of the International Astrophysics Series is to provide a collection of authoritative volumes dealing with the main branches of Astrophysics and Radio Astronomy. The need for such a series of books has arisen because of the great developments which have taken place in these fields of work during recent years.

The books will be suitable for both specialists and students. Some of the titles may have a wider and more popular appeal, but this will be secondary to their main purpose, which is to assist in the teaching of Astrophysics and Radio Astronomy and in the advancement of these subjects themselves.

Authors' Preface

When examined with a sufficiently powerful telescope under conditions of good atmospheric seeing, the surface of the Sun reveals a fine structure consisting of an irregular, cellular pattern of polygonal bright elements – granules – separated by narrow dark lanes. Over the whole solar surface there are some two million granules, whose average diameter is only about $1''.5$ of arc (1100 km). The observation of such small structures is not easy, and only in the last decade or so has the application of high-resolution techniques (both from the ground and from high-altitude balloons) given us a detailed picture of the properties and mode of origin of the granulation. Our aim in this book is to present a comprehensive account of this new knowledge.

Serious interest in the fine structure of the solar surface dates back to the beginning of the nineteenth century, and in a brief historical introduction (Chapter 1) we trace the changing ideas concerning the nature of the granulation resulting first from visual examination and, later, from photographic and spectroscopic observations, during the period 1801–1957. The latter date marks the beginning of the modern era, and in Chapter 2 we give a detailed account of the knowledge derived since then of the morphology, evolution, and dynamics of the photospheric granulation. In Chapter 3 we digress slightly in order to consider the corresponding properties of certain other photospheric features (sunspot umbra granules, facular granules, and the supergranulation) which, in one way or another, are analogous to the photospheric granules.

Modern observations show unmistakably that the photospheric granulation is a basically convective phenomenon, each granule and its surrounding dark material representing a single convection cell. In fact, the granules are the visible manifestation of sub-photospheric convection currents which contribute substantially to the outward transport of energy from deeper layers and thus help to maintain the energy balance of the Sun as a whole. Actually, they play an even wider rôle since, in the upper levels of the photosphere, they are believed to give rise to waves which are partially, if not wholly, responsible for heating the overlying chromosphere and corona. At the present time it is not known whether these waves are acoustic, gravity, or magnetohydrodynamic waves; however, we have intentionally excluded from this book any discussion of the heating of the chromosphere and corona since the high-resolution observations of the chromosphere upon which any adequate discussion must properly rest are unfortunately still lacking.

In Chapter 4 we turn to a consideration of modern hydrodynamic theories of fluid convection, with the aim of providing a proper basis for interpreting the observed properties of the granulation. In pursuing this aim, we have included not only discussions of astrophysical convection in general and the solar hydrogen convection zone in particular, but also an account of recent work by a number of theoretical hydrodynamicists; much of the latter work is not sufficiently well-known to solar physicists although it throws useful light on some of the problems of solar convection. The subject matter of this chapter is inherently difficult and complex, but we have tried to develop the account in such a way as to make the subject accessible both to solar physicists and astrophysicists with no expert knowledge of modern fluid mechanics and to theoretical hydrodynamicists with no previous experience of solar physics.

The modern theory of fluid convection has certainly advanced our knowledge of the physical nature of the granulation, but the theory itself still suffers from serious deficiencies. Foremost amongst these is the absence of a treatment that takes adequate account of *non-linear interactions*. In guiding the future development of the theory, improved observations of certain crucial aspects of the granulation are likely to play a vital rôle. Some of these observations require only relatively minor improvements in existing techniques; others, on the other hand, require the use of large telescopes operating outside the Earth's atmosphere. Accordingly, we conclude the book by describing current developments in high-resolution observing methods, both ground-based and extra-terrestrial, which offer some promise of eventually bringing such observations within the realm of possibility (Chapter 5).

The Sun is in no sense a peculiar star: a dwarf of spectral class G0–2 it is – as far as we know – a typical member of the lower main sequence of the Hertzsprung–Russell diagram. If we were able to examine the surfaces of other stars of similar spectral class, we would presumably see the phenomena of the granulation and supergranulation in much the same form. In fact, stars covering a wide range of spectral class are believed to possess convective envelopes similar to that of the Sun. G, K, and M stars have a hydrogen convection zone of considerable thickness, while B and A stars have either a thin zone or none at all, the transition from a thick to a thin zone occurring at class F. Very probably the early B stars possess a helium convection zone. Among red stars, both giants and dwarfs have a deep convection zone, which in the extreme case of a late M dwarf extends all the way to the star's centre. In general a convective core is associated with a strong concentration of the thermonuclear energy generation towards the centre; the Sun is believed not to have a convective core.

In calculating the structure of stars with convection zones, astrophysicists have long been obliged to rely on a highly-simplified theory of convection, the 'mixing-length' theory. However, this treatment contains several arbitrary features and ignores virtually all details of the hydrodynamic processes occurring in a convecting fluid. The absence of a proper theory of astrophysical convection is currently recognized as a serious gap in our knowledge of the laws governing stellar structure and evolution, as M. Schwarzschild and others have repeatedly emphasized. For example, uncertainty in the choice of the mixing-length itself introduces great uncertainty into the calculation of the structure and thickness of the convection zone of a given stellar model, and even of such a basic parameter as the radius of the star as a whole.

Although this book has been written primarily for solar physicists, the authors hope that this first detailed account of the properties of the solar granulation and its physical interpretation will provide astrophysicists with the necessary observational basis for further extending and improving the theory of convection under the conditions prevailing in stars.

R. J. B.
R. E. L.

Acknowledgements

The authors wish to thank Miss Joan M. Cook, the Reference Librarian of the National Standards Laboratory, for assistance in procuring out-of-the-way literature, and Mrs S. Williams and Mr H. R. Gillett for skilful preparation of the Figures and Plates respectively.

For supplying illustrative material we thank the following persons and organizations:

Dr J. W. Evans, Sacramento Peak Observatory (Plates 2.4, 5.4; Fig. 5.6).
Dr R. Howard, Mt Wilson and Palomar Observatories (Plate 5.1).
Dr R. B. Leighton, Mt Wilson and Palomar Observatories (Plate 3.3).
Dr J. Rösch, Pic-du-Midi Observatory (Plate 2.2(*a*)).
Prof. M. Schwarzschild, Princeton University (Plate 2.1).
Carl Zeiss, Oberkochen, West Germany (Plate 5.3).

For permission to reproduce copyright material we are indebted to the Editors of the following journals: *Annual Review of Astronomy and Astrophysics*, *Applied Optics*, *Astrophysical Journal*, *Australian Journal of Physics*, *Bulletin of the Astronomical Institutes of the Netherlands*, *Journal of Fluid Mechanics*, *Publications of the Astronomical Society of Japan*, and *Zeitschrift für Astrophysik*.

Our special thanks go to a number of friends and colleagues in Germany and the U.S.A. (in addition to individuals specifically acknowledged in the text) who, by private discussions and correspondence, have helped to clarify our ideas concerning some of the difficult observational and theoretical problems dealt with in this book.

Finally, we express our gratitude to the C.S.I.R.O. Executive and Dr R. G. Giovanelli, Chief of the Division of Physics, for permission to publish this work and for continued support of the authors' research programmes.

Commonwealth Scientific and Industrial Research Organization
National Standards Laboratory
Sydney, Australia

R. J. Bray
R. E. Loughhead

Contents

Plates

CHAPTER 1

Historical Introduction

1.1 Early Visual Observations of the Photospheric Granulation

No serious attempt to elucidate the fine structure of the solar surface was made until the beginning of the nineteenth century, when the problem attracted the attention of the famous English astronomer Sir William Herschel (1738–1822). Observing the Sun with a reflector of about 10-foot focal length fitted with a speculum mirror of his own manufacture, Herschel interpreted what he saw in the light of his own highly exotic views regarding the habitability of the Sun. 'On a former occasion', he wrote in 1801, 'I have shewn that we have great reason to look upon the Sun as a most magnificent habitable globe'. Herschel pictured the solar disk as being covered by *corrugations* which, he said, 'I call that very particular and remarkable unevenness, ruggedness, or asperity, which is peculiar to the luminous solar clouds, and extends all over the surface of the globe of the Sun. As the depressed parts of the corrugations are less luminous than the elevated ones, the disk of the Sun has an appearance which may be called mottled'. From this description it seems clear that Herschel did not resolve the individual photospheric granules as such but rather the large-scale pattern of brightness fluctuations which appears when the granulation is viewed with inadequate resolving power or under mediocre conditions of atmospheric seeing.

After Herschel, interest in the problem of the fine structure of the solar disk languished until, in the early 1860's, it suddenly became the centre of a spirited controversy involving many of the foremost solar observers of the day. The originator of the controversy was the English engineer, James Nasmyth (1808–1890), who is remembered as the inventor of the steam hammer and as an assiduous observer of the Moon. At his factory at Bridgewater, near Manchester, Nasmyth had all the facilities for casting and polishing specula. With his largest mirror, a 20-inch, he constructed a Cassegrain–Newtonian telescope on an altazimuth mounting. After his retirement to Penshurst in Kent, Nasmyth used this telescope to make many observations of sunspots and the solar photosphere, using a high-powered eyepiece and choosing moments when the seeing was best. These observations led him to announce in 1862 that the Sun's surface was actually covered by a compact pattern of thin bright filaments shaped much like *willow-leaves*.

According to Nasmyth, the willow-leaves were extremely regular in shape and size but crossed one another in all possible directions, the dark interstices between them giving rise to the mottled appearance of the disk. Nasmyth's conception of the willow-leaf pattern is illustrated in Plate 1.1, which is a reproduction of a drawing that he made on June 5, 1864, of a sunspot group and the surrounding photosphere.

Nasmyth's announcement of his discovery of the willow-leaf pattern sparked off a number of searching discussions throughout the astronomical world. One experienced English observer, the Rev. William Dawes (1799–1868), flatly denied the existence of such structures, while the famous Italian astronomer Father Secchi (1818–1878) derived from his own observations a picture of the photospheric fine structure which was much closer to reality. He described the solar surface as covered with a multitude of small bright features, which he likened to *grains*, separated by lanes of darker material. The grains were similar in size but differed considerably in shape. Plate 1.2 is a reproduction of one of Secchi's own drawings taken from his treatise *Le Soleil*, showing the pattern in the neighbourhood of a small sunspot pore.

While the morphological details of Secchi's drawing constitute a fair approximation to the truth, the same cannot be said of his attempt to measure the sizes of the individual grains. He derived a figure of about 0″.3 of arc, whereas modern observations yield a representative value for the diameter of the granules of 1″.5 (cf. Section 2.2.2). Similar measurements were made by another assiduous visual observer, S. P. Langley (1834–1906), who in 1867 was appointed director of the Allegheny Observatory in the U.S.A. and later became secretary of the Smithsonian Institution and a notable pioneer in the new science of aerodynamics. Using the 13-inch Allegheny refractor, he found that the average diameter of the grains was between 1″ and 2″ but claimed that, at the moments of best seeing, the individual grains appeared as conglomerates of smaller elements not exceeding 0″.3 or 0″.4 in width.

The visual observer whose description of the photospheric fine structure came closest to the truth was the Englishman, Sir William Huggins (1824–1910), who is remembered primarily for his important contributions to the field of stellar spectroscopy. According to Huggins the grains, which he preferred to call by the name *granules* suggested by Dawes in 1864, were distributed over the entire solar surface and were more or less round or oval in shape, although more irregular forms did occur. Their diameter he estimated to lie between 1″ and 1″.5 of arc, in agreement with the modern figure. Huggins' note published in 1866 in the *Monthly Notices* of the Royal Astronomical Society effectively terminated the controversy over Nasmyth's willow-leaves. Unfortunately, however, Huggins went beyond his realistic description of the individual granules to claim that they were grouped to form a variety of fantastic shapes and patterns; these he illustrated by a

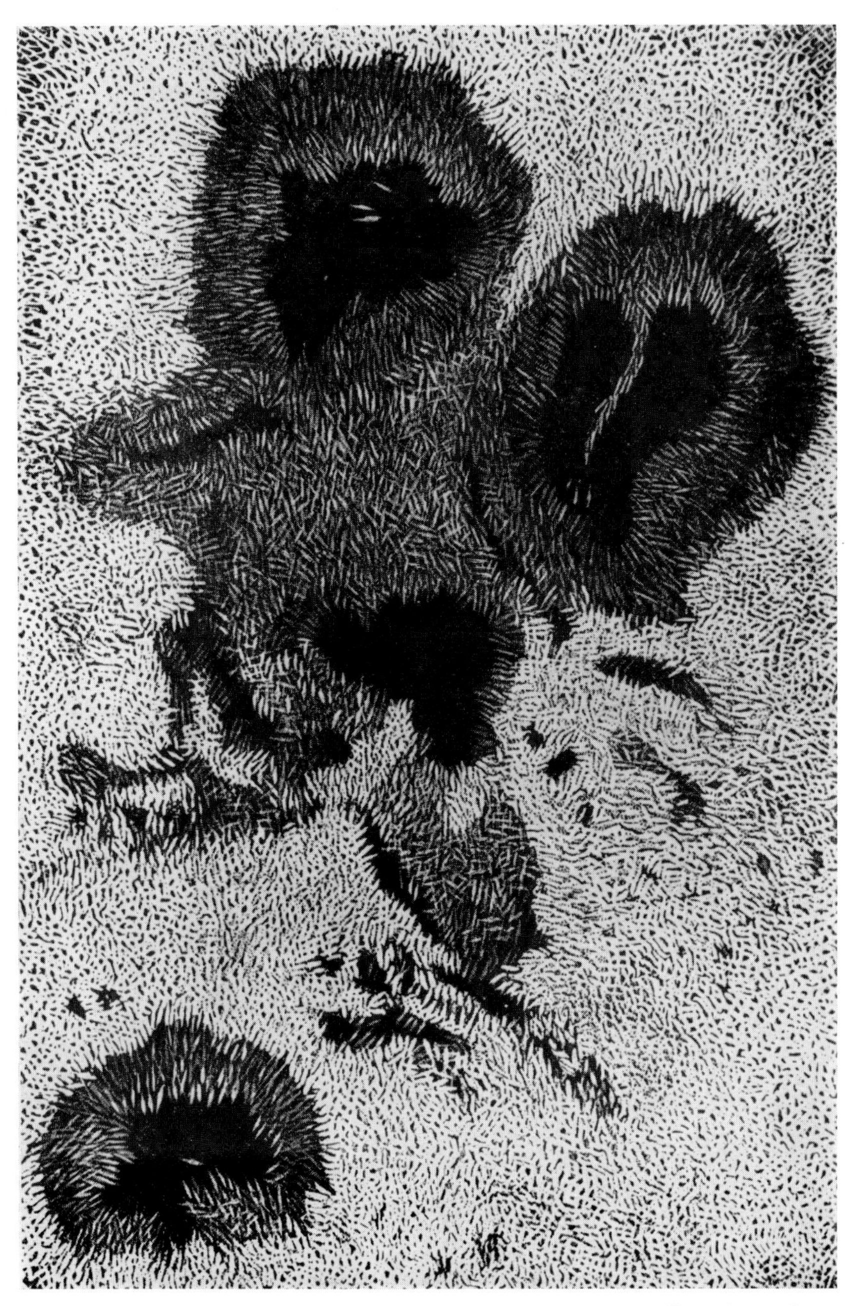

PLATE 1.1. Drawing of a large sunspot group and the surrounding photosphere made by James Nasmyth on June 5, 1864, illustrating his conception of the appearance of the solar disk as a concentrated pattern of thin bright filaments or 'willow-leaves'. According to Nasmyth, the willow-leaves were extremely regular in shape and size but crossed one another in all possible directions, the dark interstices between them giving rise to the mottled appearance of the disk.

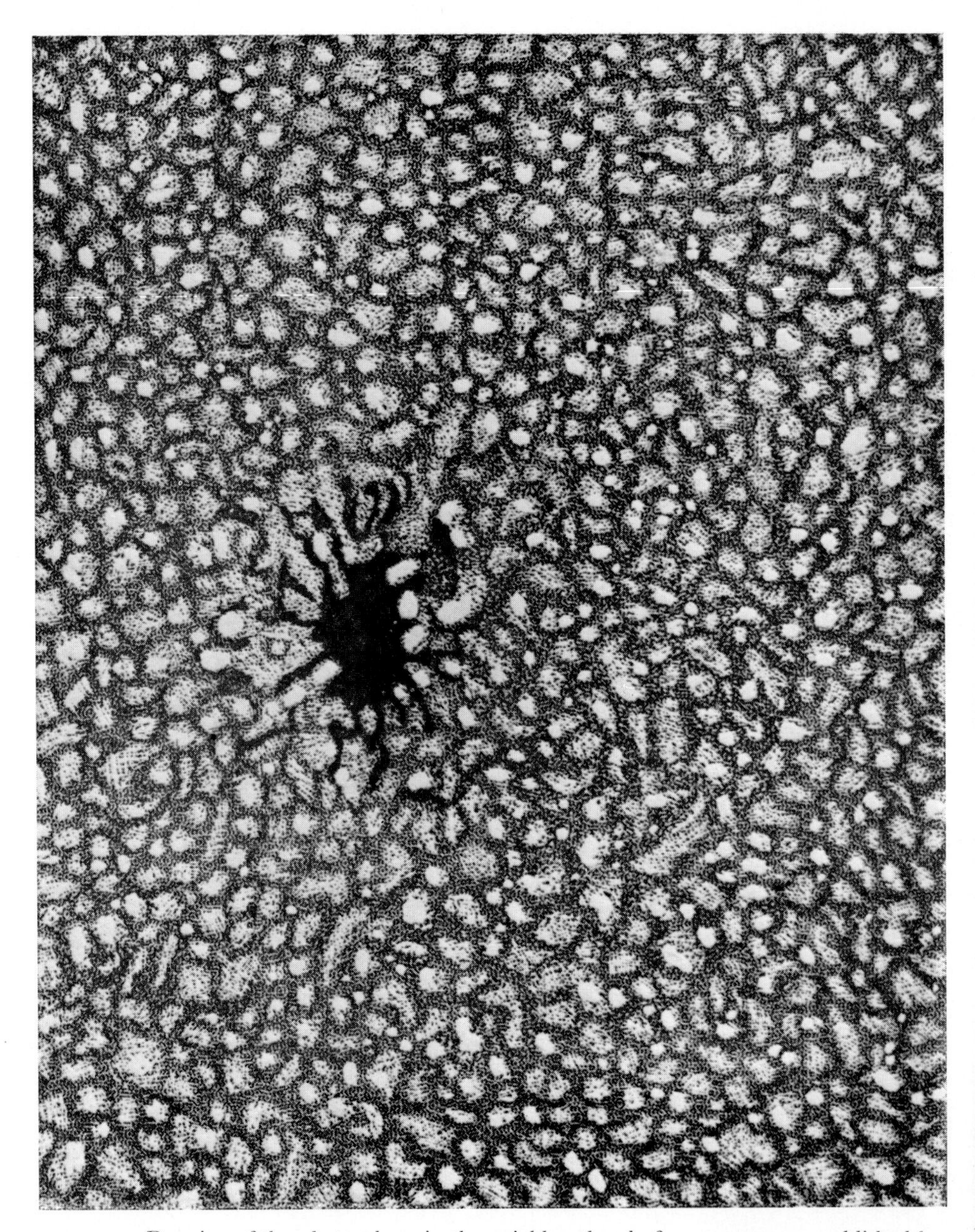

PLATE 1.2. Drawing of the photosphere in the neighbourhood of a sunspot pore published by Father Secchi in his book *Le Soleil* (1875). He pictured the solar surface as covered with a multitude of small bright features ('grains') separated by lanes of darker material. Secchi's grain structure bears a fair resemblance to the photospheric granulation pattern although, unfortunately, no scale was given on the original drawing.

PLATE 1.3. Pierre Jules Janssen, the famous French astronomer, who was the first successfully to photograph the photospheric granulation. His statue stands in the grounds of the Meudon Observatory, with the city of Paris in the background.

PLATE 1.4. Reproduction of part of a photograph of the photospheric granulation obtained by Janssen on April 1, 1894. Although marred by seeing, it shows clearly that the granulation consists of a well-defined pattern of bright granules mostly 1–2″ of arc in diameter, separated by lanes of darker material.

drawing, which the interested reader will find reproduced in Young's book, *The Sun*.

1.2 Pioneering Photographic Observations of Janssen, Hansky, and Chevalier

On August 13, 1877, the French astronomer Pierre Jules Janssen (1824–1907) rose before a meeting of the Academy of Sciences in Paris and announced that he had successfully photographed the photospheric granulation. Born the son of an eminent musician and educated at the University of Paris, Janssen achieved fame by his discovery in 1868 that with the aid of a spectroscope it was possible to see prominences outside of an eclipse.[1] As a result of this work he was appointed director of a new astrophysical observatory set up at Meudon, in the vicinity of Paris (cf. Plate 1.3). There, using a refractor of 13·5 cm aperture, he quickly brought the art of high-resolution solar photography to a high degree of perfection. In fact, when the American astronomer Langley visited Meudon in 1877, he remarked that during his many years of visual observations there had been only five or six occasions when he had seen photospheric detail with a clarity equal to that of Janssen's photographs – and then only for a few seconds at a time.

Plate 1.4 is a reproduction of part of a photograph obtained by Janssen on April 1, 1894. It shows clearly that the photospheric granulation in the central region of the solar disk consists of a well-defined pattern of bright granules with diameters lying mostly in the range 1–2″ of arc, separated by lanes of darker material. The resolution is, in fact, comparable to that of modern granulation photographs taken with telescopes of similar aperture. A number of factors contributed to Janssen's success: the choice of a telescope of the type and size which we now know to be particularly suited to the task of high-resolution solar photography; the use of an enlarging lens to obtain a large effective image diameter (30 cm) with a relatively short optical path; and the employment of a 'flying-slit' shutter to achieve very short exposure times. Yet despite these notable advances in technique, Janssen's observations contributed very little to our knowledge of the properties of the individual photospheric granules, principally because he was side-tracked into devoting most of his effort to studying a large-scale pattern of distortions occurring on many of his photographs, to which he gave the name *réseau photosphérique*. Janssen believed this pattern to be an actual feature of the solar surface, produced by violent movements of the granules in certain localized areas. However, the work of many subsequent observers has conclusively shown that the *réseaux* are due entirely to the effects of poor atmospheric seeing.

In all, Janssen's photospheric observations extended over a period of some twenty years. They were published in collected form in 1896 in a volume

[1] The same discovery was made independently by Sir Norman Lockyer.

which also contains reproductions of twelve of his original photographs. Plate X of this collection is well known even today: it is the one on which the granulation appears to show a striking resemblance to a very regular, polygonal convection pattern. (Part of this photograph has been reproduced by Kiepenheuer, 1953: cf. Fig. 13.) However, in the light of modern knowledge, we must regard this particular photograph with a good deal of suspicion. In the first place, the granulation pattern appears to be *too* regular, whereas we now know that there is actually a considerable diversity in the sizes and shapes of the individual granules (cf. Plate 2.1). Secondly, a careful examination of Janssen's original reproduction shows that in the regions of the photograph where the regular polygonal appearance is most marked, the individual features have diameters lying mostly in the range 2–4″ of arc, according to the scale given by Janssen. These features are therefore about twice the size of normal photospheric granules and we must consequently attribute their origin to some spurious effect of unknown cause.[2]

The first observer to point out the atmospheric origin of Janssen's *réseau photosphérique* was the young Russian astronomer Alexis Hansky (1870–1908). Educated at the University of Odessa, he spent some time at the Meudon Observatory before returning home to Russia where, in 1905, he was appointed an assistant astronomer at the Pulkovo Observatory near Leningrad. There, using a conventional astrograph and an enlarging camera, he turned his attention to high-resolution photography of the solar disk. His main interest lay in the photospheric granulation, and he succeeded in obtaining granulation photographs showing somewhat better resolution than those of Janssen himself. Moreover, Hansky deserves special credit for realizing the importance of obtaining sequences of granulation photographs taken at short time intervals apart in order to study changes in the granules with time. Although his attempts to obtain sequences were only partially successful, Hansky nevertheless derived an estimate of about 5 min for the mean lifetime of the photospheric granules – about one-half the correct value (cf. Section 2.2.7). On the other hand, he erroneously concluded that the granules execute horizontal oscillations about a mean position with speeds of up to 4 km/sec, failing to appreciate that their apparent lateral displacements from photograph to photograph were due – like Janssen's *réseaux* – entirely to the effects of atmospheric seeing.

In 1908 Hansky went to the Crimea, where the Pulkovo Observatory had recently established a southern station, with the intention of continuing his observations of the granulation under more favourable climatic conditions. However, just as his programme was about to start, he tragically lost his life while bathing in the Black Sea.

[2] One possible explanation may lie in the action of surface tension forces during the processing of the original plate, which was of the wet collodion type. Drying paint films, for example, often display regular, convection-like patterns produced by variations in surface tension (cf. Section 4.4.3).

A third pioneer in the art of high-resolution solar photography was Father Stanislas Chevalier (1852–1930), for many years the director of the Zô-Sè Observatory in China. This observatory was founded as a branch of an older Jesuit observatory situated at Zi-Ka-Wei on the outskirts of Shanghai. The Zô-Sè Observatory was built on a low hill some 15 miles from Shanghai and was equipped with twin 40-cm refractors of 7 m focal length carried on the same equatorial mounting, one designed for visual work and the other for photography. Although the instrument was brought into operation in 1901, observations of the Sun did not start until 1904. Chevalier's photographs, like those of Janssen and Hansky, clearly demonstrated that the photospheric granulation consists of a pattern of bright granules mostly 1–2″ of arc in diameter, separated by lanes of darker material. However, although Chevalier devoted much effort to the study of the granulation, his work added little to the existing knowledge of its properties. In fact, Chevalier's claim to recognition rests more on his contributions to the study of the fine structure of sunspots than on his work on the granulation.

As a result of the pioneering photographic observations of Janssen, Hansky, and Chevalier, by 1914 the existence and nature of the photospheric granulation was firmly established. However, the time was not yet ripe for a proper physical interpretation of the phenomenon. For example, Chevalier was content to conclude a paper on the photosphere published in the *Astrophysical Journal* in 1908 in the following vein:

> 'Let us admit . . . that the granules are the summits of a fleecy stratum of condensed particles, with or without any horizontal movement; and that the stratum is subject to undulatory movements; the summits of the waves will then present the same succession of changes, their relative position varying in every direction and with any velocity. The short, quickly changing waves of a choppy sea may possibly give us a faint imitation of what is realized on a gigantic scale and in a very different element in the solar photosphere.'

Despite their achievement in removing any doubt possibly remaining as to the existence and form of the granulation pattern, Janssen, Hansky, and Chevalier failed to exploit the full potentialities of high-resolution photography. Moreover, they did not realize just how much physical information could be gained from observations of this kind. In fact, nearly half a century was to elapse before the new technique, in an improved form, was fully utilized as a research tool for the study of the solar photosphere (cf. Section 1.6).

1.3 Strebel's Discovery of the Polygonal Nature of the Granules

Following the pioneering work of Janssen, Hansky, and Chevalier, interest in high-resolution photography of the photospheric granulation waned and it was not until 1933 that an important new observational discovery was announced. This came as a result of the efforts of a German physician and amateur astronomer, Hermann Strebel (1868–1943), who, in collaboration with a technician, B. Schmidt, photographed the granulation with a 35-cm horizontal reflecting telescope belonging to the Munich Observatory, diaphragmed down to 20 cm. Amongst other things, Strebel paid particular attention to the important question of the true shape of the granules and reached the conclusion, to quote his own words, '*das tatsächlich die Granula der Hauptsache nach polygonale Gebilde sind*, das selbst ausgesprochene Dreiecksquerschnitte häufig vorkommen'.[3] The polygonal outlines of the granules are clearly evident on some of the photographs published by Strebel, the best of which show areas where the resolution is, in fact, comparable to that of the best modern photographs (cf. Section 2.2.1).

Strebel's observations demonstrated more clearly than ever before the striking resemblance of the photospheric granulation to an irregular, cellular *convection pattern*. However, Strebel's discovery, despite its importance and its publication in a well-known international journal (the *Zeitschrift für Astrophysik*), apparently attracted little attention and, as the years passed, was largely forgotten. In fact, as we shall see in Section 1.6, the irregular, polygonal character of the granulation pattern was not re-discovered until 1957, when photographs of the photosphere were for the first time obtained with a resolution surpassing that achieved by Schmidt and Strebel a quarter of a century before.

1.4 Identification of the Granules as Convection Cells

The essential foundation for the modern convective theory of the origin of the photospheric granulation was laid by the distinguished German astrophysicist Albrecht Unsöld, who in 1930 showed that, as a consequence of the increase in hydrogen ionization with depth, there must exist a zone of convective instability directly beneath the visible photospheric layers. As we shall explain in more detail in Section 4.5.1, an elementary volume of gas moving upwards through the hydrogen ionization zone is heated by the release of ionization energy. The buoyancy of the element is thus increased and it continues its upward journey. In this way convection currents are generated, to which Unsöld attributed the origin of the photospheric granulation (and, incidentally, of sunspots as well).

Unsöld himself did not attempt to give any detailed picture of the exact mechanism involved, but this task was soon taken up by other workers. In 1933 H. Siedentopf (1906–1963) suggested that the granules represent globules or bubbles of hot gas pushing their way upwards through cooler descending material. He pointed out that the value of the Reynolds number under the conditions obtaining in the hydrogen convection zone exceeded

[3] Translated, this reads: '*that the granules are actually in the main polygonal structures*, and even definitely triangular structures frequently occur'.

the critical figure for the onset of turbulence and concluded that the convection currents must therefore be turbulent in character.[4] Siedentopf based his ideas on the 'mixing-length' theory of turbulence introduced shortly before by the famous German aerodynamicist L. Prandtl. The fundamental basis of this theory is the assumption that the convective energy is carried by 'turbulent eddies' which part with their energy and momentum after travelling a distance equal to the mixing-length. Siedentopf identified the granules with Prandtl's 'turbulent eddies', and his ideas were refined and elaborated by a number of later workers, including R.v.d.R. Woolley, L. Biermann, C. de Jager, and E. Böhm-Vitense.

Today, the mixing-length or bubble theory of convection is no longer regarded as valid, since it ignores virtually all details of the hydrodynamic processes that occur in a convecting fluid. However, it has survived as a relatively simple method of calculating zero-order approximations to models of the convection zones of the Sun and stars, although in recent years even this application has been subjected to an increasing amount of criticism (see Section 4.2.3).

A very different but much more realistic picture of the type of convective motion responsible for the granulation was put forward in 1936 by the English astronomer H. H. Plaskett. He drew attention to the classic laboratory experiments on convection in thin liquid films performed by H. Bénard at the beginning of the century[5] and pointed out the striking resemblance between the appearance of the granulation and the cellular convection patterns observed in liquids heated from below. This resemblance led Plaskett to suggest that each granule and the surrounding intergranular region be identified with a Bénard cell in the unstable hydrogen ionization zone. The idea of identifying the granules with convection cells was, in fact, a direct forerunner of present-day theoretical research into the nature of the convective processes responsible for the granulation, a topic which forms the subject matter of Chapter 4. However, owing perhaps to the formidable mathematical difficulties associated with the hydrodynamic theory of cellular convection, Plaskett's suggestion was at the time largely ignored by theoreticians who, for more than two decades, continued to concentrate their attention on the mixing-length theory. The one noteworthy exception was J. Wasiutynski who, in a long and rather unorthodox treatise published

[4] This rather naïve argument would hardly be accepted today. The Reynolds number criterion for the onset of turbulence is no more than an empirical rule valid in the case of the forced flow of an incompressible fluid through a pipe; there is no reason to suppose that it continues to hold under the vastly different conditions envisaged by Siedentopf.

[5] Attention had previously been drawn to Bénard's work by H. Deslandres in 1910 in connexion with the interpretation of features observed in H- and K-line spectroheliograms. Recent work (see Section 4.4.3) has shown that under the conditions of Bénard's experiments the driving mechanism was almost certainly provided by *surface tension* forces rather than by convective buoyancy forces. This misinterpretation does not, of course, affect the historical importance of Bénard's experiments.

in 1946, severely criticized the mixing-length theory and championed the Bénard cell interpretation.

1.5 The First Spectroscopic Measurements of Granule Velocities; Attempts to Interpret the Granules as 'Turbulent Eddies'

In the years immediately following the end of the Second World War considerable advances were made in the production of plane diffraction gratings of large size and high light-efficiency. This development was pioneered at the Mt Wilson Observatory by H. D. Babcock and was subsequently carried on by his son, H. W. Babcock, now the director of the Mt Wilson and Palomar Observatories. Besides having great spectroscopic resolving power, the gratings made by the Babcocks were blazed to diffract a large percentage of the incident light into a given order and so enabled high-dispersion solar spectra to be taken with much shorter exposure times than was previously possible. With the shorter exposures the degrading effect of atmospheric seeing on the spatial resolution of the spectra was reduced, and in this way it became possible to obtain spectra with a definition approaching that shown by good-quality direct photographs of the photosphere – albeit only under the best seeing conditions.

One of the first large solar instruments to benefit from the advent of the blazed diffraction grating was the 75-foot spectrograph of the 150-foot solar tower at Mt Wilson. In 1949 a new grating, ruled under the supervision of H. D. Babcock, was installed in the spectrograph and with it R. S. Richardson succeeded in obtaining for the first time spectra having a spatial resolution sufficient to resolve individual photospheric granules. These spectra showed prominent bright and dark streaks running parallel to the dispersion, which were produced by the granules and intergranular dark spaces falling on the spectrograph slit. The streaks themselves were intersected by the solar absorption lines in a definite zigzag manner, indicating the presence of both upward and downward velocities at the points of intersection (cf. Plate 2.4). The magnitude of the velocities was of the order of a few tenths of a kilometre per second.

Working in collaboration with the theoretical astrophysicist Martin Schwarzschild, of the Princeton University Observatory, Richardson used one spectrum showing exceptionally fine definition to compare the Doppler displacements along the length of the slit with the brightness fluctuations at the corresponding points in the continuum. *A priori*, on the basis of a convective explanation of the origin of the granulation, one would have expected a strong correlation between the brightness and velocity variations, the hot granules moving upwards and the cool intergranular material downwards. On the contrary, however, Richardson and Schwarzschild found that the observed correlation was rather weak, only the narrow regions of high upward velocity appearing to be systematically brighter than average.

At the time this result may have seemed to throw some doubt on the identification of the granules as convection cells. Since then, however, the problem of granule velocities has been attacked by a large number of other workers using more powerful observing techniques and, as a result, it is now known that velocity observations of the type made by Richardson and Schwarzschild, when interpreted in the light of modern knowledge, actually throw no doubt on the convective origin of the granulation. Nevertheless, the questions of the true nature of the small-scale velocity field observed in solar absorption lines and of its relationship to the granulation have proved to be of considerable complexity; both topics are discussed at some length in Section 2.4.

One fact which greatly puzzled Richardson and Schwarzschild was the smallness of the measured granule velocities compared with estimates previously obtained by a variety of indirect means, such as studies of the photospheric curve of growth and line profile analyses. This consideration led them to advance the hypothesis that the motions in the photosphere, far from being basically convective, were in fact a manifestation of a *large-scale turbulence*. On this basis they attributed the discrepancy in the velocity estimates to the fact that the various determinations referred to 'turbulent elements' of different sizes.[6] Their argument is perhaps best summarized in their own words:

> 'Laboratory experiments have shown that the state of turbulence of a gas cannot be described well by one mean size of the turbulent elements but rather has to be described by a whole continuous spectrum of sizes. In every case of turbulence there appears to exist one size of elements which possesses the highest average velocity. Elements with sizes larger than those of the fastest elements show a rapid decrease of average velocity with element size. On the other hand, toward smaller element sizes the average velocity falls off slowly. More particularly, under conditions usually fulfilled in astronomical cases this fall-off is governed purely by the process of dissipation of bigger elements into smaller elements. In this process, according to Kolmogoroff, the random turbulent velocity decreases as the reciprocal cube root of the element size.'

Using Kolmogoroff's law, Richardson and Schwarzschild combined the results of the various velocity determinations mentioned above to derive a 'spectrum of turbulence' for the solar photosphere. The form of the turbulent velocity spectrum suggested that the diameter of the turbulent elements of highest average velocity should be about 100 to 200 km – less than one-fifth of the diameter of the photospheric granules visible on good-quality direct

[6] Actually, there is no real discrepancy: the 'velocities' derived from measurements of line profiles or equivalent widths are not to be identified with the actual velocities of individual granules but indicate merely the existence of non-thermal motions in the region of line formation. Moreover, they provide no evidence for fully developed turbulence in the strict aerodynamic sense [see, for example, Loughhead and Bray, 1959].

photographs. Richardson and Schwarzschild therefore concluded that their measured values of the granule velocities probably represented merely the statistical effect of the higher velocities of small, unresolved turbulent elements, whose existence had hitherto been unsuspected.

Richardson and Schwarzschild also pointed out that these small, energetic elements or granules should have a greater brightness than those hitherto observed and were thus led to predict the existence of granules very much smaller and brighter than any previously resolved on direct photographs. This prediction attracted considerable attention and, in fact, it was in order to test it that, in 1955, Schwarzschild decided to build a 12-inch balloon-borne telescope to photograph the Sun at a height well above the disturbed layers of the atmosphere responsible for poor seeing (cf. Section 1.6).

The modern reader may feel that Richardson and Schwarzschild erected rather an elaborate superstructure upon somewhat flimsy foundations. However, in order to place their work in its proper historical perspective, one has to appreciate the remarkable extent to which the thinking of many astrophysicists in the years following the end of the Second World War was influenced by the considerable developments then taking place in the theory of aerodynamic turbulence. The advance which attracted the attention of astronomers most was A. N. Kolmogoroff's formulation of similarity laws to describe the statistical equilibrium of the small-scale components of turbulence.[7] Under appropriate circumstances these laws enable specific predictions to be made about observable properties of turbulent velocity fields even in the absence of a proper understanding of their exact mode of origin. Despite the fact that Kolmogoroff's laws are strictly applicable only to an incompressible fluid in a state of fully-developed, homogeneous, isotropic turbulence, there was a rush of indiscriminate attempts to apply them over the whole gamut of astrophysical problems. These ranged from Richardson and Schwarzschild's attempt to construct a complete turbulent velocity spectrum for the solar photosphere to C. F. von Weizsäcker's suggestion that the galaxies or clusters of galaxies represent the largest eddies of a primordial cosmic turbulence!

There is another aspect of Richardson and Schwarzschild's work which, viewed with historical hindsight, seems even more remarkable than the prevailing pre-disposition to the uncritical acceptance of theories based on turbulence. This is the fact that these workers chose to ignore the overwhelming evidence against the existence of large-scale turbulence in the photosphere provided by the results of more than seventy years of granulation photography. These included not only the observations of Janssen, Hansky, Chevalier, and Strebel, already described, but also good-quality photographs obtained by a number of more modern observers, including P. C. Keenan at the Yerkes Observatory, and P. ten Bruggencate, H. von Klüber, and

[7] Kolmogoroff's work was published in the U.S.S.R. in 1941 but did not become generally known outside that country until after the end of the war.

others at the Potsdam Astrophysical Observatory (cf. Table 2.7). The very existence of a distinct cellular pattern of bright granules on a dark background revealed by these observations was, *ipso facto*, conclusive proof that any motions associated with the granulation were basically well-ordered and certainly not predominantly turbulent in character. Richardson and Schwarzschild's failure to recognize this fact was tantamount to questioning the validity of the observational evidence for the existence of the granulation pattern as such. Indeed, following their lead, a number of other workers including, for example, F. N. Frenkiel, A. Skumanich, and M. S. Uberoi, erroneously concluded from actual photometric measurements that the brightness fluctuations were random and that a cellular pattern did not exist.

Under the circumstances, it is hardly surprising that by the mid-1950's there was widespread confusion among solar physicists as to the true appearance of the photosphere. Some workers remained convinced of the reality of the granulation and, as we shall see in the next section, made plans for improved observations, whereas others hesitated to admit its existence. A striking illustration of the state of affairs then prevailing is provided by the words of three very experienced observers at the McMath–Hulbert Observatory, R. R. McMath, O. C. Mohler, and A. K. Pierce, who began a paper published in the *Astrophysical Journal* in 1955 under the title 'Doppler shifts in solar granules' with the sentence: 'In titling this note we do not necessarily imply the existence of granules as such, but, because of the ease of discussion and widespread use in the literature, we retain the term.' Fortunately, however, as we shall see in the next section, such confusion was destined to be short-lived.

1.6 Beginning of the Modern Era of High-Resolution Granulation Observations

The beginning of the modern era of high-resolution granulation photography antedates the first successful spectroscopic observations of the granules by nearly a decade. It goes back to the early 1940's when the French astronomer Bernard Lyot (1897–1952), working at the Pic-du-Midi Observatory, pioneered the application of the cinematographic technique to the photography of the solar photosphere. By taking a large number of photographs at intervals short compared with the lifetime of the granules, he was able to obtain a few comparatively unaffected by seeing. Lyot himself went no further than to demonstrate the value of the technique, but in recent years cinematographic observations of the granulation have been carried on by J. Rösch at the Pic-du-Midi with notable success; much of Rösch's work is described in the chapter that follows.[8]

[8] The credit for introducing the cinematographic technique as a research tool in solar physics properly belongs to the late R. R. McMath (1891–1962) and his associates at the

In 1957 the full power of the cinematographic method for granulation photography was convincingly demonstrated by R. B. Leighton at the Mt Wilson Observatory. Working in the early morning when the seeing conditions at the 60-foot solar tower are at their best, he obtained sequences of high-quality photographs of the granulation using the full 12-inch aperture of the telescope. Like Strebel's photographs, Leighton's observations showed the granules as bright features of various shapes separated by narrow lanes of darker material, whose apparent width was comparable with the resolving limit of the telescope, $0''.4$ of arc. The basic appearance of individual granules remained unaltered from photograph to photograph. As Leighton pointed out, these observations demonstrated conclusively that the granules were to be identified with *convection cells* and not with the eddies of any large-scale turbulence. Originally a physicist at the California Institute of Technology but now on the staff of the Mt Wilson and Palomar Observatories, Leighton has in recent years gone on to develop ingenious new techniques for 'photographing' magnetic and velocity fields on the surface of the Sun, which in turn have led to observational discoveries of fundamental importance (cf. Sections 2.4.2 and 3.4).

The next development took place in Australia when, in 1957, the Physics Division of the Commonwealth Scientific and Industrial Research Organization brought into operation a 5-inch photoheliograph specifically designed for high-resolution cinematography of the solar photosphere and sunspots. The observations obtained with this instrument were of sufficient quality to enable the development of individual granules to be followed from photograph to photograph. It was found that the majority of granules show a remarkable absence of systematic change over most of their lifetimes. This stability strongly supported Leighton's conclusion that the motions within the granules themselves are basically laminar rather than turbulent, and therefore the view that the granules were to be identified with convection cells rather than 'turbulent eddies'. Moreover, the Australian observations, while not capable of showing granules as small as the very bright elements predicted by Richardson and Schwarzschild (Section 1.5), revealed no strong correlation between the brightness and size of individual granules: in fact, it was found that bright granules are just as frequently larger as smaller than average (cf. Table 2.2).

Parallel to the development of improved methods of observing the granulation from the ground, a radically different approach to the problem was being pioneered in England and France by D. E. Blackwell, D. W. Dewhirst, and A. Dollfus. Following earlier unsuccessful experiments from an aircraft

McMath–Hulbert Observatory, where motion-picture films of prominences and other chromospheric phenomena were obtained as early as 1933. Subsequent experiments with 'white-light' cinematography indicated that the new technique might also be ideal for recording changes in the photospheric granulation, but it was never systematically used for this purpose at the McMath–Hulbert Observatory.

flying at 22,000 feet, these workers constructed a solar telescope for operation from a manned balloon and carried out several flights to heights of 20,000 feet. Their balloon photographs were much better than those obtained at random from the ground but were nevertheless inferior to the best ground-level photographs. However, the manned flights did serve the useful purpose of showing that a balloon telescope needed to be operated at greater heights if the residual effects of atmospheric seeing were to be entirely avoided.

Meanwhile, in the U.S.A. a team of individuals and organizations under the direction of Martin Schwarzschild was building a 12-inch balloon-borne solar telescope for automatic operation in the stratosphere, a complex and expensive undertaking which became known as 'Project Stratoscope I'. The original specific aim was to test Richardson and Schwarzschild's prediction of the existence of small, very bright granules – hitherto unresolved – with which they claimed the most energetic 'turbulent elements' of the photosphere were to be identified. In the latter part of 1957 several successful flights were carried out at heights in the vicinity of 80,000 feet, where 96 per cent of the Earth's atmosphere lay below the telescope. During these and later flights granulation photographs of unsurpassed definition were obtained, one of which is shown in Plate 2.1. However, as the reader may see for himself, they show no predominance of small, very bright granules and thus, by an ironic twist of fate, directly contradict Richardson and Schwarzschild's original prediction! Instead, the appearance of the solar surface is that of an irregular pattern of polygonal bright granules, mostly 1–2″ of arc in diameter, separated by narrow lanes of dark material. This is of course identical to the picture provided by the ground-based observations of Strebel and Leighton, but to Schwarzschild, as he generously admitted, the pattern came as a complete surprise.

In view of the developments described above, the year 1957 may be taken as marking the beginning of a new era in the study of the solar granulation. Since then tremendous advances have been made in our observational knowledge of its properties, while theoreticians have devoted much attention to the problem of elucidating the nature of the convective processes responsible for its origin. The results of all this work are described in the succeeding chapters of the book.

1.7 Chronological Summary

1801. W. Herschel uses the term 'corrugations' to describe the mottled appearance of the solar disk.

1862. Announcement of Nasmyth's 'willow-leaf' pattern.

1864. Dawes introduces the term 'granule'.

1866. Publication of a paper by Huggins ends controversy over Nasmyth's willow-leaves.

1877. Granulation successfully photographed by Janssen.

1896. Publication of Janssen's collected observations.
1908. Hansky estimates mean lifetime of granules to be about 5 min.
1914. Publication of Chevalier's collected observations of the granulation.
1930. Unsöld attributes the origin of the granulation to convection currents in the hydrogen ionization zone.
1933. Announcement of Strebel's discovery of the polygonal shapes of the granules.
1933. Siedentopf formulates a theory of the granulation based on Prandtl's mixing-length theory of turbulent convection.
1936. H. H. Plaskett identifies the granules as Bénard-type convection cells.
1949. Richardson obtains spectra showing the Doppler shifts of the granules.
1950. Richardson and Schwarzschild identify the granules as the eddies of a large-scale aerodynamic turbulence.
1953. First reliable determination of granule lifetimes made by C. Macris (cf. Section 2.2.7).
1955. Various workers claim that the solar surface shows random brightness fluctuations, not a cellular pattern.
1957. Rösch publishes granule observations made at the Pic-du-Midi.
1957. High-resolution photoheliograph brought into operation near Sydney by the C.S.I.R.O.
1957. Leighton re-asserts convective origin of the granulation.
1957. Granulation photographed from a manned balloon.
1957. Project Stratoscope I yields granulation photographs of unsurpassed definition.

REFERENCES

BABCOCK, H. D., and BABCOCK, H. W. [1951] 'The ruling of diffraction gratings at the Mount Wilson Observatory', *J. Opt. Soc. Amer.* **41,** 776.

BATCHELOR, G. K. [1953] *The Theory of Homogeneous Turbulence.* (Cambridge Univ. Press).

BURGERS, J. M., and THOMAS, R. N. [1958] *Preface* to 'Proceedings of the Third Symposium on Cosmical Gas Dynamics', *Rev. Mod. Phys.* **30,** 908–910.

CHANDRASEKHAR, S. [1949] 'Turbulence – a physical theory of astrophysical interest', *Astrophys. J.* **110,** 329.

CHEVALIER, S. [1908] 'Contribution to the study of the photosphere', *Astrophys. J.* **27,** 12.

CHEVALIER, S. [1914] 'Étude photographique de la photosphère solaire', *Ann. Obs. Zô-Sè* **8,** C1.

DAWES, W. R. [1864] 'Results of some recent observations of the solar surface, with remarks', *Mon. Not. R.A.S.* **24,** 161.

EVANS, J. W. [1963] 'Motions in the solar atmosphere', *Sky and Tel.* **25**, 321.

FRENKIEL, F. N., and SCHWARZSCHILD, M. [1955] 'Additional data for turbulence spectrum of solar photosphere at long wavelengths', *Astrophys. J.* **121**, 216.

HANSKY, A. [1908] 'Mouvement des granules sur la surface du Soleil', *Mitt. Pulkovo Obs.* **3**, 1.

HERSCHEL, W. [1801] 'Observations tending to investigate the nature of the Sun, in order to find the causes or symptoms of its variable emission of light and heat; with remarks on the use that may possibly be drawn from solar observations', *Phil. Trans. Roy. Soc.* 1801, Part 1, p. 265.

HUGGINS, W. [1866] 'Results of some observations on the bright granules of the solar surface, with remarks on the nature of these bodies', *Mon. Not. R.A.S.* **26**, 260.

JANSSEN, J. [1896] 'Mémoire sur la photographie solaire', *Ann. Obs. Meudon* **1**, 91.

KIEPENHEUER, K. O. [1953] 'Solar activity'. (*The Sun*, ed. G. KUIPER, p. 322; Univ. Chicago Press).

KING, H. C. [1955] *The History of the Telescope.* (Griffin: London).

LANGLEY, S. P. [1874] 'On the minute structure of the solar photosphere', *Amer. J. Sci. Arts,* Series 3, **7**, 87.

LANGLEY, S. P. [1874] 'On the structure of the solar photosphere', *Mon. Not. R.A.S.* **34**, 255.

LEIGHTON, R. B. [1957] 'Some observations of solar granulation', *Publ. Astron. Soc. Pac.* **69**, 497.

LOUGHHEAD, R. E., and BRAY, R. J. [1959] ' "Turbulence" and the photospheric granulation', *Nature* (*Lond.*) **183**, 240.

MCMATH, R. R., MOHLER, O. C., and PIERCE, A. K. [1955] 'Doppler shifts in solar granules', *Astrophys. J.* **122**, 565.

NASMYTH, J. [1862] 'On the structure of the luminous envelope of the Sun', *Manchester Lit. Phil. Soc. Mem.*, Series 3, **1**, 407.

PLASKETT, H. H. [1936] 'Solar granulation', *Mon. Not. R.A.S.* **96**, 402.

RICHARDSON, R. S., and SCHWARZSCHILD, M. [1950] 'On the turbulent velocities of solar granules', *Astrophys. J.* **111**, 351.

RUBASHEV, B. M. [1964] *Problems of Solar Activity*, Chap. 2. (Nauka Publishing House: Moscow–Leningrad; N.A.S.A. Technical Translation F-244: Washington).

SECCHI, A. [1875] *Le Soleil*, 2nd ed., vol. 1. (Gauthier-Villars: Paris).

SCHWARZSCHILD, M., and SCHWARZSCHILD, B. [1959] 'Balloon astronomy', *Sci. Amer.* **200**, No. 5, p. 52.

SIEDENTOPF, H. [1933] 'Konvektion in Sternatmosphären. I', *Astron. Nachrichten* **247**, 297.

SKUMANICH, A. [1955] 'On bright-dark symmetry of solar granulation', *Astrophys. J.* **121**, 404.

STREBEL, H. [1932] 'Sonnenphotographische Dokumente', *Z. Astrophys.* **5**, 36.

STREBEL, H. [1933] 'Beitrag zum Problem der Sonnengranulation', *Z. Astrophys.* **6,** 313.

UBEROI, M. S. [1955] 'On the solar granules', *Astrophys. J.* **122,** 466.

UNSÖLD, A. [1930] 'Konvektion in der Sonnenatmosphäre', *Z. Astrophys.* **1,** 138.

WASIUTYNSKI, J. [1946] 'Studies in hydrodynamics and structure of stars and planets', *Astrophysica Norvegica* **4,** Chap. 4.

YOUNG, C. A. [1895] *The Sun.* (Kegan Paul: London).

CHAPTER 2

The Morphology, Evolution, and Dynamics of the Photospheric Granulation

2.1 Introduction

The appearance of the granulation in the central region of the solar disk is well illustrated in Plate 2.1, which is an enlargement of a very high-quality photograph obtained by M. Schwarzschild and his collaborators with a 12-inch balloon-borne telescope on August 17, 1959.[1] This photograph shows that the granulation consists of a *cellular* pattern of bright elements on a darker background. The majority of the granules appear to have diameters in the range 1–2″ of arc (725–1450 km) and are separated by narrow dark lanes, whose apparent width often does not exceed a few tenths of a second of arc. In places, however, there are relatively large areas of dark intergranular material, which seem to result from the absence – presumably temporary – of one or more granules. These occasional dark regions are characteristic features of the granulation pattern, and should not be confused with *pores* (small sunspots with no penumbra), which are not only darker but also very much longer-lived [Bray and Loughhead, 1964: p. 69].

It is instructive to compare the appearance of the granulation on Plate 2.1 with that on Plate 2.2, which shows two photographs taken with ground-based telescopes. The first of these (Plate 2.2(*a*)) was obtained by J. Rösch on May 14, 1959, with a 38-cm (15-inch) refractor at the Pic-du-Midi Observatory. It is of slightly lower resolution than the stratospheric photograph, but the polygonal outlines of the granules and the narrowness of the dark lanes separating them are again well shown. The second photograph (Plate 2.2(*b*)) was obtained by the authors on January 10, 1960, with the Sydney 5-inch photoheliograph (for a description of this instrument, see Bray and Loughhead, 1964: pp. 27–31). On this photograph the granules have lost their polygonal appearance as a result of the lower resolution, although their diversity in shape and size is still apparent. Moreover, the

[1] For full information on the design and operation of the stratospheric telescope, the reader should consult the references cited in Section 5.4.1.

dark lanes between the granules are now much wider and more diffuse. In this regard, it is important to emphasize that in the velocity measurements subsequently described in this chapter, the effective spatial resolution is comparable to that of Plate 2.2(*b*) rather than to that of Plate 2.1 or 2.2(*a*).

Our aim in the present chapter is to give a critical and comprehensive account of current observational knowledge of the properties of the granulation pattern as a whole and of the individual granules. Information obtained from high-resolution direct photography is described in Sections 2.2 and 2.3, while spectroscopic observations of granule velocities and magnetic fields are dealt with in Section 2.4. We shall be concerned solely with the *photospheric* granulation in this chapter; related phenomena (the supergranulation, sunspot umbra granules, and facular granules) are reserved for the chapter that follows. Moreover, little or no attempt is made to give a theoretical explanation of the various observed features, the whole question of the origin of the granulation and the interpretation of its properties being dealt with in Chapter 4.

We begin by describing the properties of the individual photospheric granules (Sections 2.2.1 to 2.2.8), dealing successively, among other things, with their shape, diameter, 'cell size', contrast, lifetime, and evolution. In Section 2.3 we consider the important question of how close to the limb the granulation can still be perceived, and hence how far the convection currents responsible penetrate up into the higher layers of the photosphere. The observations show unmistakably that the granules penetrate well into the upper region of the photosphere which, according to the modern theory of the hydrogen convection zone (cf. Section 4.3.2), is convectively *stable*. This phenomenon is akin to the penetration ordinarily observed in naturally-occurring convection.

Actual measurements of granule velocities in both the convectively stable and unstable regions are discussed in Sections 2.4.1 to 2.4.3. Good-quality spectrograms indicate that the majority of bright features in the continuum are associated with upward velocities and the majority of dark features with downward velocities – as is to be expected for a convective process. An unexpected fact, however, is that the velocity field in the upper photosphere is *oscillatory* in character, the velocity at any given point varying in an almost sinusoidal fashion with a period close to 5 min. The scale of the velocity pattern, although roughly comparable to that of the granulation, appears to be systematically somewhat larger. At the moment the exact relationship between the photospheric velocity field and the granulation is not completely clear, and observations of higher spatial resolution are required to elucidate it further.

In Section 2.4.4 we consider the question of whether there is any relationship between the granulation and the *magnetic* fields known to be present in the photosphere. Despite great observational difficulties, spectroscopic observations made to resolve this question appear to indicate that, although the

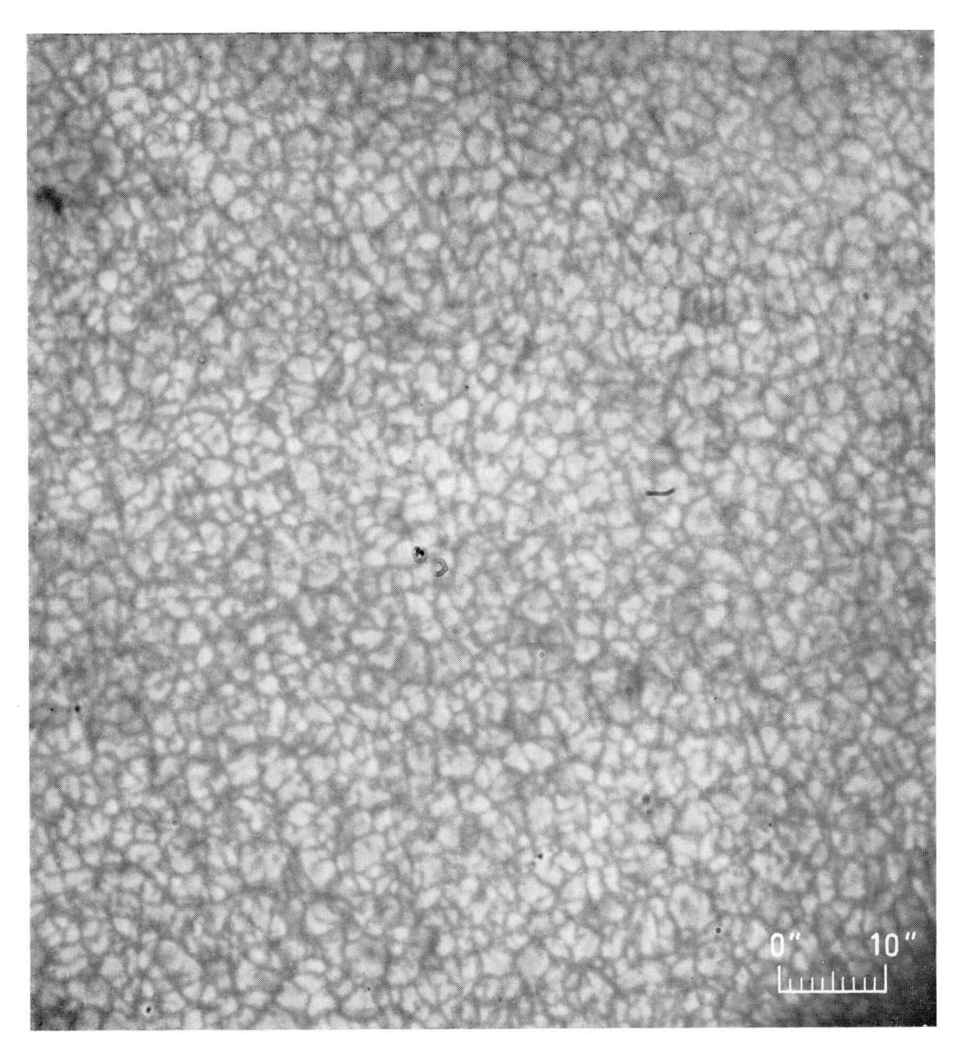

PLATE 2.1. Photograph of the photospheric granulation obtained by M. Schwarzschild and his collaborators with a 12-inch balloon-borne telescope on August 17, 1959. (*By courtesy of Project Stratoscope of Princeton University, sponsored by O.N.R., N.S.F., and N.A.S.A.*)

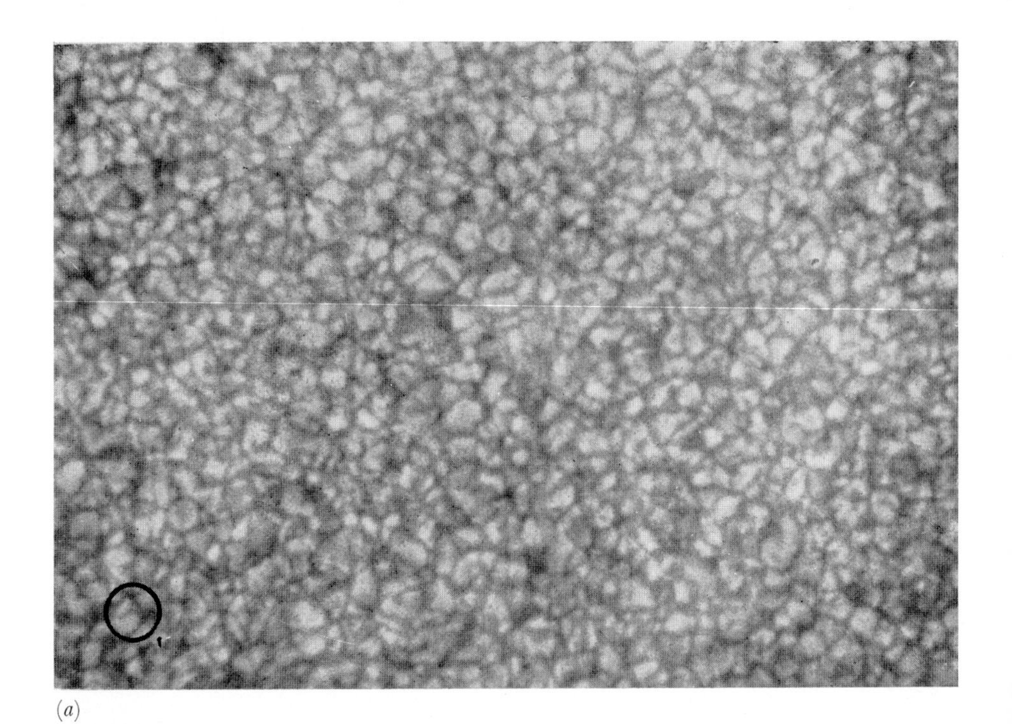

(*a*)

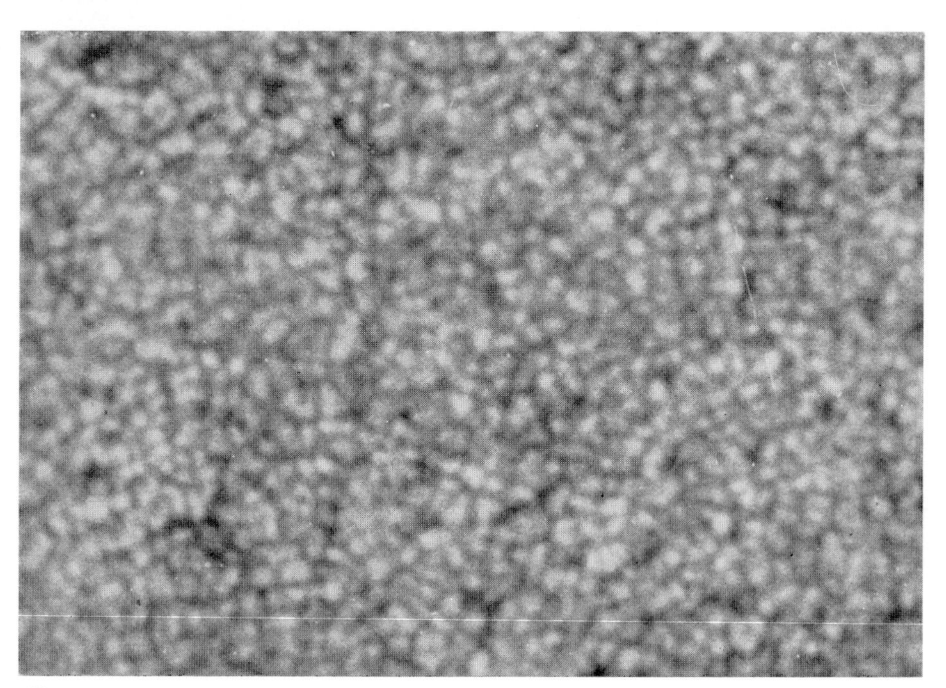

(*b*)

PLATE 2.2. The photospheric granulation.

(*a*) Photograph obtained by J. Rösch on May 14, 1959, with a 15-inch refractor at the Pic-du-Midi Observatory.

(*b*) For comparison, a photograph of lower resolution obtained with the Sydney 5-inch photoheliograph on January 10, 1960.

Both photographs are on the same scale; the diameter of the circle is 5″ of arc.

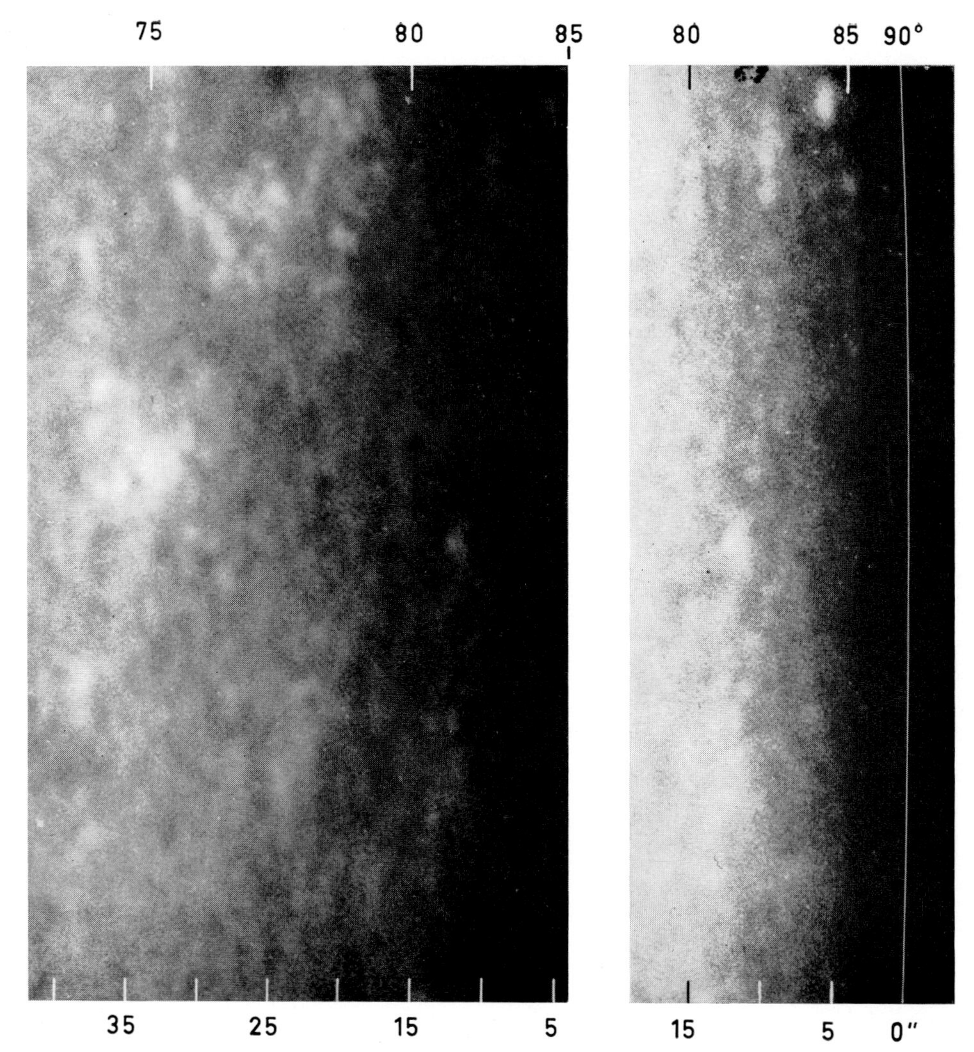

PLATE 2.3. Granulation near the extreme solar limb, photographed with the Sydney 5-inch photoheliograph. Both prints were made from the same original negative; the white line indicates the position of the actual limb, derived from the negative. The upper scale gives the heliocentric angle, the lower scale the distance from the limb in seconds of arc.

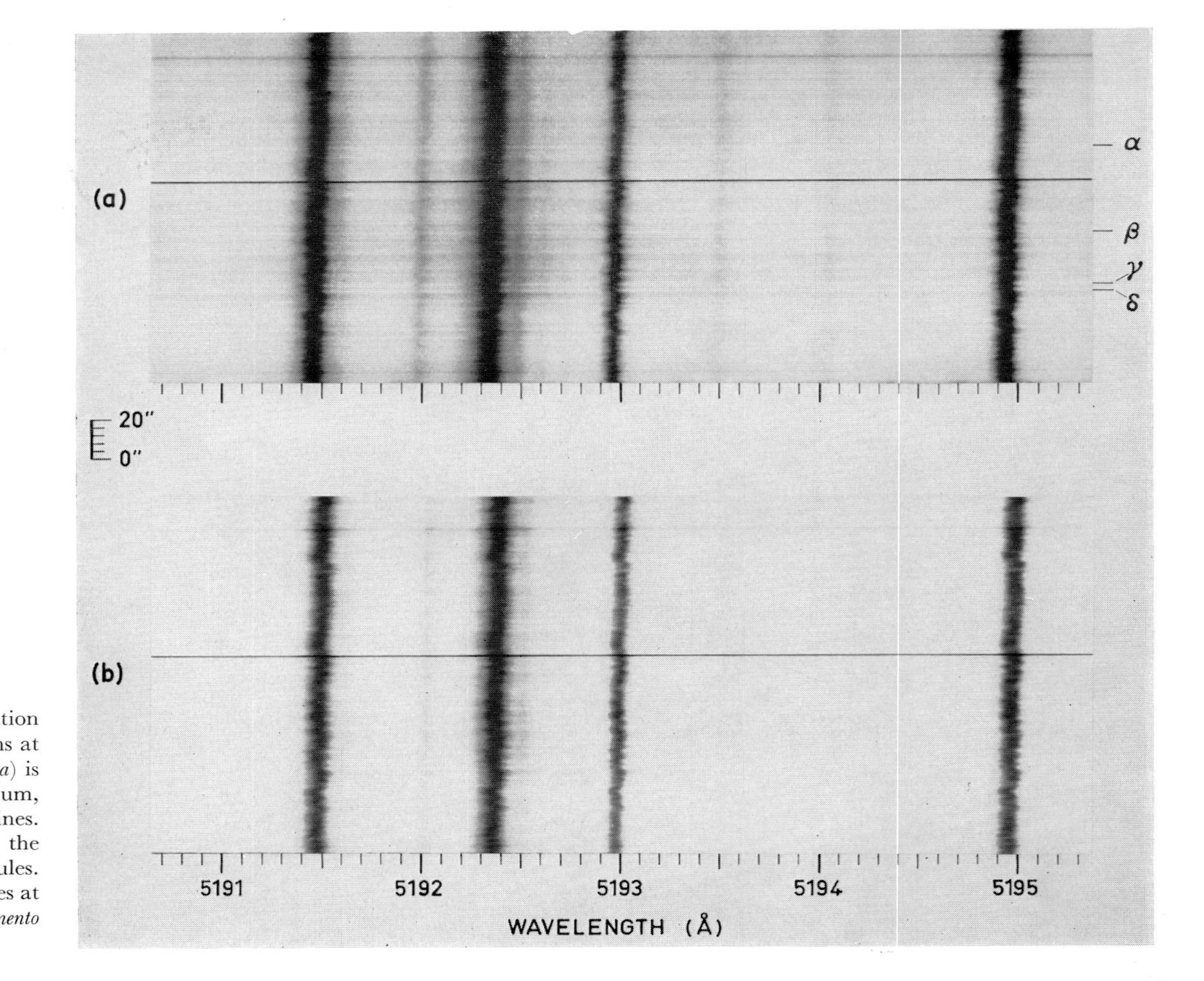

PLATE 2.4. High-resolution granulation spectrogram obtained by J. W. Evans at the Sacramento Peak Observatory. (*a*) is printed to show detail in the continuum, (*b*) to show detail at the core of the lines. The letters α, β, γ, and δ indicate the positions of four prominent granules. Note the presence of upward velocities at positions γ and δ. (*By courtesy of Sacramento Peak Observatory.*)

weak fields outside activity regions show evidence of fine structure, any correlation with the granulation is either weak or entirely absent. The granulation usually appears to remain unaffected by the stronger fields associated with activity centres, although definite disturbances have occasionally been observed in the photosphere between new and developing sunspot pores.

For the convenience of the reader, the chapter ends with a chronological summary (Table 2.7) of the various observational investigations from 1896 onwards which have contributed substantially to our present knowledge of the photospheric granulation.

2.2 Properties of the Photospheric Granules

2.2.1 SHAPE

It is evident from Plate 2.1 that many of the granules have very irregular shapes. Polygonal and elongated outlines are very common, and the granules fit neatly together in the pattern like the stones in a crazy-paving path. In other words, in most cases adjacent granules have parallel boundaries on their common sides, the dark channel separating them being of uniform width. The fact that many granules have polygonal outlines was first pointed out by Strebel [1933], whose best photographs show areas in which the resolution is comparable to that of modern stratospheric photographs such as Plate 2.1 [see Strebel, 1932: Fig. 1; 1933: Fig. 5]. However, Strebel's discovery apparently attracted little attention and as the years passed by was largely forgotten (cf. Section 1.3). A number of later workers [Macris, 1953; Bray and Loughhead, 1958b; Blackwell, Dewhirst, and Dollfus, 1959] established that a significant proportion of the granules are non-circular, but their photographs lacked sufficient resolution to reveal the characteristic straight sides of many of the granules, well shown on Plate 2.1. In fact, not until the advent of the stratospheric photographs was the true nature of the granulation pattern generally appreciated.

To summarize, the granulation can succinctly be described as an irregular, cellular pattern of bright elements separated by narrow, dark channels. This basic observational fact provides the chief reason for regarding the granulation as a convective phenomenon (cf. Section 4.5.1).

2.2.2 DIAMETER

Any theoretical discussion of the photospheric granulation requires a knowledge of the value of some parameter expressing the scale of the pattern. At first sight it might seem that the average granule diameter would be a convenient parameter to use. Unfortunately, direct measurements of the diameters of the individual granules provide only a rough guide to their true dimensions. In fact, the measurement of granule size is actually a complex *photometric* problem involving not only the photographic contrast but also the instrumental profile of the telescope and, in the case of ground-based observations, of the atmosphere. Only when the influence of these factors is accurately known can the true dimensions be inferred. The difficulty of measuring granule diameters has been similarly emphasized by Rösch [1959].

Examination of Plate 2.1 shows that many of the granules appear to have diameters in the range 1–2″ of arc. Accordingly, if one is content with a rough guide to the true granule diameter, a representative, although not necessarily *average*, value – uncorrected for instrumental effects – is 1″.5 = 1100 km. This figure is close to the values given by many workers before photographs of the quality of Plate 2.1 had been obtained (for references, see Table 2.7). For example, the present authors [Bray and Loughhead, 1958b], on the basis of their own photographs, gave the figure of 1″.3 of arc for 'average-sized' granules and 1″.8 for 'large' granules. Actual measurements of stratospheric photographs have since been made by Schröter [1962], who finds an average diameter of 1″.2–1″.3 for granules in the undisturbed photosphere and 1″.0 for granules in the immediate vicinity of sunspots.[2]

Schwarzschild [1959, 1961] has attempted to determine the average granule diameter by means of a *correlation analysis*. Defining the average diameter as twice the distance over which 'the autocorrelation of the photospheric intensity fluctuations' drops to half its peak value, he finds a diameter of only 700 km.[3] However, inspection of Plate 2.1 shows that although there are many granules having a diameter as small as 700 km, this figure (which is also quoted in the *Landolt–Börnstein Tables* – see Voigt, 1965: p. 98) is too low to be regarded as a truly representative value. There is in fact a large dispersion in granule size: the smallest granules visible on Plate 2.1 which are nevertheless fully distinguishable – i.e. completely surrounded by dark material – have an apparent diameter of about 0″.4 of arc (300 km), a figure comparable with the resolving limit of the telescope used. The largest granules, on the other hand, have a diameter (largest dimension) of about 3″.2 of arc (2300 km).

It is worth pointing out that a close visual inspection of Plate 2.1 reveals traces of structure within these larger granules. However, it is not sufficiently prominent to cause any difficulty in identifying the granules as individual entities.

2.2.3 'CELL SIZE'; TOTAL NUMBER OF GRANULES ON THE SUN

In view of the difficulty of measuring granule diameters, the present authors [Bray and Loughhead, 1959] and independently, Rösch [1959], have used instead the *mean cell size* of the pattern, defined as the average distance between the centres of adjacent granules, as a convenient quantitative parameter for characterizing the scale of the pattern. This parameter is independent of photographic contrast and instrumental resolution, provided

[2] According to Harvey and Ramsey [1963], the average granule diameter appears to be much the same in the near ultra-violet as in the visual region of the spectrum.

[3] Using a similar method, Leighton [1963] finds a value of only 640 km.

the individual granules are actually resolved. As we shall see in Chapter 4, the cell size plays an important role in theoretical discussions of convection. In Chapter 4 the cell size of a convective mode is denoted by the symbol λ, while the quantity $K = 2\pi/\lambda$ is termed the *horizontal wave-number* of the mode in question.

The authors' results are shown in Fig. 2.1, which gives the distances between the centres of adjacent granules, derived from measurements of a group of ninety-two granules on a good-quality photograph taken with the

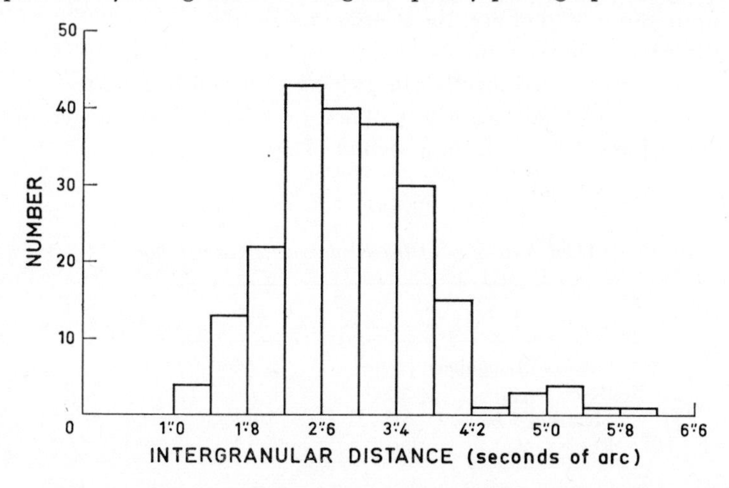

Fig. 2.1. Cell size of the photospheric granulation pattern. The histogram gives the distribution of the distances between the centres of adjacent granules (corrected for foreshortening), measured for a group of 92 granules on one of the authors' photographs. It is evident that the granulation has a well-defined and rather narrow distribution of cell sizes: 70 per cent of the values lie between 2".2 and 3".8 of arc. The mean value derived from this photograph is 2".9; however, the average of all modern determinations is 2".5 (cf. Table 2.1).

Sydney 5-inch photoheliograph. It is evident that the granulation pattern has a well-defined and rather narrow distribution of cell sizes: in fact, 70 per cent of the values lie between 2".2 and 3".8 of arc. The mean value derived from this photograph is 2".9. The long tail extending out to 6".2 reflects the presence in the pattern of the occasional dark elements mentioned in Section 2.1. The distribution is truncated at 1".0, the effective resolving limit of the telescope.

The cell size distribution found by Rösch [1959] is qualitatively similar to that obtained by the authors. It is more symmetrical, but still shows a narrow tail extending out to about 5".0 of arc. The granulation pattern is again found to have a well-defined, narrow distribution of cell sizes: the values are strongly concentrated about a mean of 2".0, 95 per cent of the intergranular distances lying between 1".0 and 3".0. The mean value of 2".0 found by Rösch is significantly smaller than that found by the authors (2".9).

It seems likely that this discrepancy is partly due to a difference in the methods of performing the measurements, Rösch's measurements being made on a *composite* photograph obtained by the superposition of many photographs taken within a short time interval. However, in a later note Rösch [1962] gives a larger value for the mean cell size, namely $2''.5$–$2''.6$.

Finally, Macris and Banos [1961] have derived values of the mean cell size from fourteen high-quality photographs of the granulation taken by various workers between the years 1880 and 1960. The individual values range from $2''.0$ to $2''.9$ of arc, the average being $2''.5$.

All the various measurements of the mean cell size of the photospheric granulation are collected together in Table 2.1; it will be seen that the best estimate at present available is $2''.5$ of arc, i.e. 1800 km, the uncertainty in this value being a few tenths of a second of arc.[4]

TABLE 2.1

Mean Cell Size of the Photospheric Granulation

REFERENCE	VALUE
Bray and Loughhead [1959]	$2''.9$
Rösch [1959]	$2''.0$
Macris and Banos [1961]	$2''.0$–$2''.9$
Rösch [1962]	$2''.5$–$2''.6$
Average	$2''.5$ = 1800 km

Adopting the value of 1800 km for the mean cell size, we can now calculate the average area A of each convection cell, and hence the total number of granules on the surface of the Sun, N. Assuming, arbitrarily, that the cells are hexagonal in shape, we obtain $A = 2{\cdot}8 \times 10^6$ km^2 and $N = 2{\cdot}2 \times 10^6$. This latter figure is in reasonable agreement with the values obtained by various workers from actual counts of the numbers of granules in measured areas of the solar disk (for references, see Table 2.7).

C. Macris and his co-workers have attempted to show that the total number of granules on the Sun [Macris and Elias, 1955] or alternatively, the mean cell size [Macris and Banos, 1961], depends on the phase of the solar cycle. However, in view of the errors inherent in the determination of these parameters (cf. Table 2.1), this result should be viewed with reserve. In fact, it has yet to be established that any of the properties of the photospheric granulation show any dependence on the phase of the solar cycle.

[4] No estimate based on stratospheric photographs has yet been published, although the authors understand that the necessary measurements have recently been carried out by K. Birkle at the Fraunhofer Institut. Many of the smaller granules visible on stratospheric photographs would fail to appear on the photographs upon which the estimates in Table 2.1 are based. It may be, therefore, that the average figure given above is slightly too large.

2.2.4 DIVERSITY IN SIZE AND BRIGHTNESS

Although the majority of the granules appear to have diameters in the range 1–2″ of arc (725–1450 km), it is also evident that some have diameters of less than half a second of arc, while others exceed several seconds (see Plate 2.1). Moreover, it will be noticed that the larger granules appear to be individual structures and not merely complexes of smaller granules packed closely together, although some of them do appear to show just a suspicion of structure which only a higher resolution could fully elucidate.

Good granulation photographs often show isolated regions where the smaller granules seem to predominate [Blackwell, Dewhirst, and Dollfus, 1959; Edmonds, 1960]. However, these appear to be chance associations which gradually disappear as new granules form and others decay.

The individual granules also show a considerable diversity in their *brightness*. The brightness differences are perhaps somewhat better shown in Plate 2.2(*b*) than in Plate 2.1: among granules of comparable size it is easy to find some which are distinctly brighter than average and others distinctly fainter than average. Bahng and Schwarzschild [1961a] remark that reproductions of the stratospheric photographs are misleading on this point. Although many of them suggest that most of the granules reach a fairly uniform level of brightness, inspection of the original photographs or the measured frequency distribution of the intensity fluctuations shows that this is not correct.

TABLE 2.2

Classification of Photospheric Granules

BRIGHTNESS	SIZE			
	Large	Average	Small	Total
Bright	12	23	2	37
Medium	23	50	19	92
Faint	1	6	4	11
Total	36	79	25	140

It is of interest to enquire what correlation, if any, exists between the *size* and *brightness* of the granules. This question has been studied by the authors during the course of an investigation into changes in the shape, size, and brightness of the granules during their observed lifetimes (Section 2.2.8). As a consequence of limited resolving power, it was possible to classify the granules only in a rather crude and qualitative way; therefore the size categories were restricted to 'large', 'average', and 'small', and the brightness categories to 'bright', 'medium', and 'faint'. In all, 140 granules were selected for study.

Table 2.2 gives the results of the classification. Considering large and average-sized granules together, the table shows that bright granules are about one-half as numerous as those of medium brightness and five times as numerous as faint ones. Particularly noteworthy is the almost complete absence of large, faint granules. In the case of small granules, bright granules are very rare and less numerous than faint ones. While the results for small granules may be affected by limited resolution, it is significant that the stratospheric photographs, taken with a telescope of over twice the resolving power, also show that small, bright granules are rather rare (cf. Plate 2.1).

It is possible that the (weak) correlation between brightness and size suggested by these results is simply a consequence of the greater radiative cooling time to be expected for the larger granules. If so, the diversity in brightness is directly related to the diversity in size. On the other hand, the diversity in size (and shape) itself can have only a hydrodynamic explanation. Many authors have suggested that the irregular appearance of the granulation reflects the fact that it represents a convective process well beyond the state of marginal instability – called 'non-stationary convection' by Schwarzschild [1959]. This topic is further discussed in Chapter 4.

2.2.5 MEASUREMENT OF CONTRAST

The granular contrast may be defined as the quantity

$$C = \frac{I_{\max} - I_{\min}}{\frac{1}{2}(I_{\max} + I_{\min})},$$

where $I_{\max}$ and $I_{\min}$ represent the brightness of the granules and the intergranular material respectively. Knowledge of this parameter, together with its centre-limb variation, would allow the derivation of an inhomogeneous photospheric model, i.e. one that gives exact expression to horizontal as well as vertical variations in such physical quantities as the temperature, density, pressure, absorption coefficient, etc. The non-uniform radiative transfer theory necessary for such a derivation is in fact already in existence (see Section 4.6.3). It is unfortunate, therefore, that the quantity C cannot be reliably determined from present observations.

The difficulty lies in the inadequate resolution of existing photographs. The problem of determining the granular contrast is almost exactly analogous to the familiar problem of measuring the true central intensity of a Fraunhofer line. This is possible only when the width of the instrumental profile of the spectrograph is substantially less than the width of the line. Similarly, in measuring the granular contrast, the instrumental profile of the telescope must be substantially narrower than the width not only of the granules themselves but also of *the dark lanes between them.* A careful scrutiny of Plate 2.1 shows that even on this photograph – taken with a 12-inch telescope above the Earth's atmosphere – the apparent width of the dark lanes is often less than $0''.5$ of arc [see also Leighton, 1963]. The true width must be even smaller, since the effect of the finite resolution is to widen the dark lanes. It follows that it must be comparable with or smaller than the theoretical resolving limit of a 12-inch telescope ($0''.4$).

In fact, in order to obtain a reliable value for the granular contrast, the following conditions must first be satisfied:

(1) the effective resolving limit of the telescope would need to be several times smaller than the true width of the dark lanes. A 50-inch telescope (resolving limit, $0''.1$) operating outside the Earth's atmosphere would probably be adequate;

(2) both the wings and the core of the instrumental profile of the telescope would need to be accurately known;

(3) in correcting the measured contrast for the effect of instrumental profile, it would be necessary to solve the integral equation of obliteration for the two-dimensional case.

Although we are not able to quote a reliable figure for the granular contrast, it is instructive to consider one careful modern attempt to obtain an estimate of this parameter, namely that of Blackwell, Dewhirst, and Dollfus [1959]. These workers made isophotometric contour maps of the granulation, from which they derived mean values for the apparent contrast between granular and intergranular material.[5] These values then have to be corrected for the finite resolution of the telescope. Blackwell and his co-workers measured the contrast transfer function of their whole telescope – objective, magnifying lens, and photographic emulsion – and gave careful consideration to the problem of correcting the measurements for instrumental distortion. The performance of the whole telescope, unfortunately, was found to be markedly inferior to that of an aberration-free system: for example, at a spatial frequency corresponding to $1''.0$ of arc, the contrast transfer function was only about one-third of its value for an ideal telescope. At a spatial frequency corresponding to $0''.5$, which we can take to be a generous upper limit to the width of the dark intergranular lanes, the contrast transfer function was found to be only about 0·05. In other words, the observed contrast of a unidimensional, sinusoidal, intensity distribution having a spatial frequency corresponding to $0''.5$ of arc would have to be multiplied by a factor of 20 to obtain the true value!

It is clear, therefore, that a very large increase in resolving power is needed before the granular contrast can be reliably determined. It would seem that this is one of the crucial problems in solar physics whose solution requires the application of large telescopes operating outside the Earth's atmosphere. Current developments in high-resolution observing methods

[5] A similar procedure has been used by Rösch [1959], who has published a two-dimensional isophotometric map of the granulation. References to earlier attempts to measure the granular contrast are given by Blackwell *et al.*

which may ultimately bring such observations within the realm of possibility are discussed in Chapter 5.

2.2.6 MEASUREMENT OF THE R.M.S. BRIGHTNESS VARIATION

As we have seen in the previous section, the photometric property of the granulation having the greatest physical interest is the contrast, since a knowledge of this parameter, together with its centre-limb variation, would lead directly to the derivation of an inhomogeneous photospheric model. However, a number of workers, deterred by the formidable instrumental difficulties involved, have attempted to measure not the contrast, but the r.m.s. brightness variation. The usual technique is to make a microphotometer tracing along some arbitrary line crossing a photograph of the granulation, and then to measure the brightness at points some fixed distance apart. This procedure has been criticized by Keenan [1939], Rösch [1959], and others, and indeed, when one bears in mind the cellular nature of the granulation pattern, it is hard to see how such a procedure could lead to results of much physical interest. A unidimensional tracing is evidently incapable of faithfully reproducing the brightness of the individual granules except in cases where, by chance, the scanning aperture happens to pass through the centre of a granule. It is true that such a tracing does to some extent reveal the diversity in the brightness of the individual granules; however, these brightness differences would be hard to separate from variations due to a chaotic mixture of unresolved dark intergranular lanes, granules photometered at their edges rather than at their centres, and so on. It is hardly surprising, therefore, that brightness variations measured in this way fit a Gaussian curve [see Schwarzschild, 1959: Fig. 5].

Such a method of approach would be warranted in the case of a random, two-dimensional brightness distribution but is quite clearly inappropriate in the case of a well-defined cellular pattern such as the granulation. However, for a description of the two most recent investigations of this type, both based on stratospheric photographs, the interested reader is referred to Bahng and Schwarzschild [1961b] and Edmonds [1962b]. References to earlier measurements of the r.m.s. brightness variation are given by Blackwell, Dewhirst, and Dollfus [1959]. Finally, it is worth mentioning that in the absence of reliable data on the centre-limb variation of the granular contrast P. R. Wilson (see Section 4.6.3) has employed Edmonds' measurements of the r.m.s. brightness fluctuation as a function of heliocentric angle as a basis for testing his own non-uniform radiative transfer theory.

2.2.7 LIFETIME

To obtain an accurate value for the lifetime of the photospheric granules it is necessary to carefully analyse a sequence of good-quality photographs of the same region, extending over a period of at least 10 min and preferably longer, say 20 min. The first adequate determination was made by Macris

[1953] using a 22-min sequence obtained by Lyot in 1943. Macris found a value of 7–8 min for the most probable lifetime, although individual values as high as 15–16 min were recorded.[6]

Another determination was later made by the present authors [Bray and Loughhead, 1958b], whose results are in broad agreement with those of Macris. However, owing to the relatively short duration of the authors' sequence (10 min), the starting and ending times of many of the granules fell outside the period of observation, suggesting that the most probable lifetime is somewhat greater than the value of 7–8 min actually found. In agreement with this conclusion, Rösch and Hugon [1959] reported that many granules

TABLE 2.3

Lifetimes of Photospheric and Sunspot Fine Structures

FEATURE	LIFETIME	REFERENCE	SECTION*
Photospheric granules	7–8 min	Macris [1953]	2.2
	~10 min	Bray and Loughhead [1958b]	
	10 min	Rösch and Hugon [1959]	
	8·6 min	Bahng and Schwarzschild [1961a]	
	8·2 min	Macris and Prokakis [1963]	
Facular granules	2 hr	Waldmeier [1940]	3·3
	2 hr	Bray and Loughhead [1961]	
Umbral granules	15–30 min	Bray and Loughhead [1959]	3.2; **3·6**
		Loughhead and Bray [1960a]	
Penumbral bright regions: Type 1	30 min	Macris [1953]	**3·5·6**
Penumbral filaments	~2 hr	Bray and Loughhead [1958a]	**3·5·4**

* Section numbers in **bold type** refer to the authors' [1964] monograph, those in ordinary type to the present work.

last for about 10 min, but did not publish a detailed analysis of their observations. Finally, Bahng and Schwarzschild [1961a] derived a mean lifetime of 8·6 min from a correlation analysis of two sequences of stratospheric photographs. Taken together, these results show that the lifetime of the photospheric granules is about 10 min. This value is considerably greater than that indicated by earlier estimates, which were based on inferior observational data.

The modern results are shown in Table 2.3 which, for comparison, also summarizes the available data on the lifetimes of the various sunspot and other photospheric fine structures. The table lists for each feature the lifetime, the source reference, and the location of a description of the feature in

[6] Rösch [1962] has recorded lifetimes as high as 20 min.

question. It is evident that the photospheric granules are much shorter-lived than the facular granules or any of the fine structures of sunspots.

In conclusion, a few remarks may be appropriate concerning the various methods of determining the granular lifetimes. The present authors had at their disposal twenty-nine good-quality photographs covering a period of 10 min 21 sec. The lifetime was found by following the individual existence of 249 selected granules from one photograph to another in the sequence. The starting or ending times of many of the granules fell outside the period of the sequence, however: for these only a lower limit to the true lifetime could be derived. A similar method was used by Macris [1953] and Macris and Prokakis [1963].

Bahng and Schwarzschild [1961a] used an ingenious method based on measurement of 'the autocorrelation of the photospheric intensity fluctuations'. The measurement was carried out as follows: a positive photographic print of the granulation corresponding to some known time $t = 0$ was placed on the baseboard of an ordinary photographic enlarger. A *negative* of the same region, but corresponding to a time $t = t_1$, was then projected onto the positive print and the amount of light reflected was measured by means of a photocell and a chart recorder. By repeating the process for a number of values of t_1 (two sequences were available, of durations 8 and 15 min), a curve representing the autocorrelation as a function of time was derived. The average granule lifetime was assumed to be equal to twice the time interval required for the autocorrelation to drop to half its peak value.

In comparing the two methods it may be mentioned that the first method, although very tedious to apply, gives directly the quantity required. Moreover, with a sufficiently long sequence, it allows a determination not only of the average or most probable lifetime but also of the *distribution* of lifetimes [cf. Macris, 1953: Fig. 6; Bray and Loughhead, 1958b: Table 3]. Finally, with photographs of adequate quality it would enable one to determine what correlation, if any, exists between the lifetimes of individual granules and their other physical characteristics, e.g. brightness, size, and shape. It suffers from the disadvantage, however, that if the photographs are of poor quality, rather subjective decisions may sometimes have to be made as to the existence or non-existence of particular granules at particular times.

On the other hand, the correlation method can be criticized for casting aside a great deal of potentially useful data, particularly when the photographs are of good quality. A second unsatisfactory feature is that the measure of the autocorrelation, although quantitative, is arbitrary and uncalibrated. Finally, in view of the fact that the autocorrelation is measured over a region of the photosphere *containing many granules*, the identification of the average granule lifetime with twice the time interval required for the autocorrelation to drop to half its peak value requires justification.

Somewhat similar correlation techniques were earlier used by ten Bruggencate and Grotrian [1936] and Leighton [1957], who obtained mean lifetimes of 3·2 and 3·9 min respectively; these values are evidently much too low. Nevertheless, in the case of Bahng and Schwarzschild's measurements the two different methods of determining the lifetimes appear to give concordant results, as Table 2.3 shows.

2.2.8 EVOLUTION

A much more difficult observational problem than the determination of granule lifetimes is the study of their evolution. This question, however, is of great interest for its bearing on the underlying hydrodynamic processes. Present-day convective theory has not yet succeeded in setting up a model of the evolution of a granule (cf. Sections 4.3.3 and 4.4.2). However, an exact knowledge of the mode of evolution of the granules and how it varies, e.g. with granule size, might be expected to assist the development of the theory by throwing some light on the physics of the non-linear interactions believed to occur.

The greater difficulty is due to the fact that the *description* of the individual granules demands photographs much better than those required for their mere *identification*. The first systematic attempt to detect changes in the brightness, size, and shape of the individual granules during their observed lifetimes was made by the authors [Bray and Loughhead, 1958b] using the 10-min sequence of photographs from which the lifetime was determined. 140 granules were first classified in regard to brightness, size, and shape according to their appearance on a very good 'master' photograph near the middle of the sequence (cf. Table 2.2), using as supporting evidence three other good photographs near the master. The same granules were then described according to their appearance on each of a number of other photographs occurring before and after the master, thus enabling the development of the individual granules to be followed from photograph to photograph over an average period of nearly 7 min. The results are summarized in Table 2.4.

Table 2.4 indicates that at this level of resolution the granules in general appear to display remarkable stability: of the 125 granules for which sufficient data were obtained, 57 per cent showed no detectable change in brightness, size, or shape over an average period of nearly 7 min, an additional 14 per cent showing only minor changes of shape. Moreover, while there is some tendency among granules showing change for size increases to predominate over decreases, brightness increases and decreases occur with equal frequency. No correlation was found between the two types of change, nor was any tendency found for brightness or size variations to occur during any particular part of the life cycle. The general stability of the granulation pattern over a period comparable with the lifetime of the granules is illustrated by Plate 2 of the authors' paper, which shows a selection of photographs from their 10-min sequence. A similar but better sequence of photographs, lasting 18 min, was later published by Rösch [1960].

Several examples of the types of changes sometimes observed in individual granules have been given by Rösch and Hugon [1959] who fail, however, to reach any definite conclusions about the general mode of evolution of the granules. In a later note, on the other hand, Rösch [1962] has asserted that in general after a granule is formed, its diameter begins to increase until it reaches about 2″ of arc, at which moment it breaks up into several small granules which vanish at the place where they appeared. This assertion evidently disagrees with the present authors' own conclusions, thus illustrating the extreme difficulty of observing granule evolution. In fact, observations

TABLE 2.4

Changes in the Photospheric Granules

TYPE OF CHANGE		NO. OF GRANULES
No change		71
Brightness	increase	12
	decrease	12
	increase and decrease*	4
Size	increase	16
	decrease	7
Change of shape		17

* These granules showed both an increase and a decrease in brightness during the period of observation.

of higher resolution are required to resolve the differences between Rösch's results and those of the present authors. Unfortunately, no information about the modes of evolution of the granules has resulted from the stratospheric observations of Schwarzschild and his co-workers, presumably because the number of photographs in the 8- and 15-min sequences they used in determining the lifetime was inadequate for the purpose.

Changes in the photospheric granules are particularly difficult to detect during their periods of formation and decay, when the granules cannot easily be identified as such. For this reason the authors' observations provide little information about the modes of formation and dissolution. Only twenty-six cases of well-defined births or deaths were recorded among the granules whose lifetimes were determined; from these the impression was gained that in general a granule develops from a vague patch of diffuse bright material, which originates in a hitherto dark area. These diffuse patches are very difficult to distinguish from granules smeared by poor seeing. The dissolution of a granule appears to occur by the reverse process, although occasionally a granule loses its identity by coalescing with another granule.

2.3 Granulation near the Extreme Solar Limb: Penetration of Granules into the Upper Photosphere

The visibility of the photospheric granulation decreases towards the limb until, finally, no trace of the pattern can be detected. A determination of the distance from the limb at which it finally disappears provides an estimate of the height of penetration of the granules into the upper photosphere [Plaskett, 1955; de Jager, 1959: cf. p. 83]. This question is of the greatest importance since, for a variety of reasons, we need to know the structure of the inhomogeneous photosphere not only in the deeper layers accessible to observation in continuous radiation, but also in the higher layers where the Fraunhofer lines originate. Until a few years ago it was generally assumed that the granules did not extend much higher than optical depth $\tau = 1$.

TABLE 2.5

Distance from the Limb at which the Granulation Disappears

ESTIMATED DISTANCE (sec of arc)	HELIOCENTRIC ANGLE	REFERENCE
10″–5″	82°–84°	Rösch [1957]
33″–21″	75°–78°	Edmonds [1960]
10″–4″	82°–85°	Loughhead and Bray [1960b]
15″–10″	80°–82°	Edmonds [1962b]

This view was derived partly from the fact that calculations based on the Schwarzschild stability criterion showed that above this level the photosphere is convectively stable (see Section 4.3.2), and partly from inadequate observations of the visibility of the granulation near the limb.

Modern observations, however, tell a different story. Rösch [1957] found that on good photographs the granulation remains visible to within less than 10″ of arc from the limb, and sometimes to less than 5″. Although Edmonds [1960] concluded on the basis of an examination of stratospheric photographs that the granulation disappears at 33″–21″, the present authors [Loughhead and Bray, 1960b] were able to confirm Rösch's value. Moreover, in a subsequent paper Edmonds [1962b] revised his estimate to 15″–10″. The various estimates are collected together in Table 2.5.

Plate 2.3, taken from the authors' paper, clearly demonstrates that the granulation remains visible very close to the limb. The plate shows overlapping regions of the Sun in the neighbourhood of the west limb: both enlargements were made from the same original negative, using intermediate negatives of slightly different densities in order partially to compensate for limb darkening. The white line on Plate 2.3(*b*) indicates the position of the actual limb, derived from the original negative.

Apart from the much brighter *facular* granules (cf. Section 3.3), a number of granules can be seen less than 10″ from the limb; in fact, one rather bright granule can be seen only 4″ from the limb. Even in regions where individual granules are hard to distinguish, the photograph gives the impression of a low contrast, foreshortened picture of the ordinary granulation.[7] No granules are visible on the original negative in the last 4″ to the limb (this region does not appear in Plate 2.3(*b*)). However, the possibility cannot be excluded that observations of higher resolution might reveal granules closer to the limb than the present limit of detection.

Let us take it as established that the granules are visible up to 5″ from the limb (heliocentric angle = 84°); then it follows that the associated convection currents extend at least up to an optical depth of $\tau = \cos 84° = 0{\cdot}1$ [cf. de Jager, 1959: p. 83]. Since the weaker Fraunhofer lines and, indeed, all but the inner cores of the stronger lines, are formed at or below this level, we should expect to find some evidence of the presence of the granulation in observations of the Fraunhofer lines. Modern velocity observations confirm this expectation, as we shall see in the next section.

The fact that the granules are visible in the region of the photosphere which, according to the Schwarzschild criterion, is convectively stable is entirely consistent with the results of extensive hydrodynamic calculations recently performed by K. H. Böhm. These calculations are based on linearized theory and are fully described in Section 4.3.2. Böhm found that, although the vertical velocities are strongly concentrated towards a thin layer at the level $\tau \simeq 1$ near the top of the convection zone, they do not go to zero there but instead penetrate into the stable photosphere above. It is interesting to note that penetration into stably-stratified regions ordinarily occurs in natural convection – for example, in the field of geophysics (see Section 4.5.2).

The published discussions of the observations described above have been criticized by Giovanelli [1961] on the grounds that they take no account of the substantial reduction in the observed granular contrast, as the limb is approached, due to increased foreshortening and finite telescope resolution. Calculating on the basis of a unidimensional contrast transfer function theory, he has concluded that telescopes of the sizes actually used could not possibly have observed the granulation as close to the limb as claimed by Rösch and by the present authors. Although Giovanelli's arguments are fallacious, as we shall see below, it is instructive to consider the basis of his objections. We can do this without using contrast transfer functions: let us take the distance apart of the centres of neighbouring granules to be 2″.5 (Section 2.2.3). Then, assuming geometrical foreshortening, granules 10″ from the limb (heliocentric angle = 82°) would appear to be separated by

[7] The foreshortening is well shown on the originals of some of the limb photographs taken by Schwarzschild and his collaborators: on these photographs the granules near the limb show a marked elongation parallel to the limb.

only $2{\cdot}5 \times \cos 82° = 0''{\cdot}35$, a figure well below the theoretical resolving limits of the telescopes used by Rösch and the present authors. Nevertheless, as Plate 2.3 shows, at this distance from the limb the granules are still well visible.

The fallacy in Giovanelli's arguments lies in his neglect of several important factors, each of which helps to preserve the visibility of the granulation near the limb:

(1) perpendicular to a radius of the solar disk there is *no* foreshortening; hence near the limb, brightness variations parallel to the limb remain in evidence. It is apparent, therefore, that a discussion based on a *unidimensional* contrast transfer function theory, or on the simple geometrical argument given above, is not adequate;

(2) there is a considerable diversity in the brightness of individual granules (Section 2.2.4). At the limb, the brighter granules are still distinguishable since on the average they are separated by distances large compared with the mean granule separation of $2''{\cdot}5$;

(3) the granules are three-dimensional entities – i.e. they have a structure in depth, part of which may become visible near the limb. The question of the visibility of the granulation near the limb is therefore not a purely geometrical problem, but one involving the theory of radiative transfer in a non-uniform medium. The necessary transfer theory is already in existence (cf. Section 4.6.3) but its application to the study of the granulation has been held up by the absence of adequate measurements of the granular contrast and its centre-limb variation.

Similar criticisms of Giovanelli's objections have been voiced by Rösch [1962].

2.4 Granule Velocities and Magnetic Fields

2.4.1 INTRODUCTION

The first spectra having a spatial resolution sufficient to resolve individual photospheric granules were obtained by R. S. Richardson in 1949, using the spectrograph of the 150-foot Mt Wilson solar tower equipped with a new Babcock grating. These spectra showed prominent bright and dark streaks running parallel to the dispersion, which were produced by the granules and intergranular dark spaces falling on the spectrograph slit.[8] The streaks themselves were intersected by the solar absorption lines in a definite zigzag manner, indicating the presence of both upward and downward velocities at the points of intersection (cf. Plate 2.4). One spectrum showing exceptionally fine definition was used by Richardson and Schwarzschild [1950] to compare the Doppler displacements along the length of the

[8] In interpreting granulation spectra one must remember that only occasionally will the slit fortuitously pass directly through the centre of a granule or intergranular dark space. At other points the slit actually receives light from a varying admixture of bright and dark areas.

slit with the brightness fluctuations at the corresponding points in the continuum. Contrary to their expectation, they found that the correlation between the velocity and brightness variations was rather weak, only the narrow regions of high upward velocity appearing to be systematically brighter than average.

Richardson and Schwarzschild's data were later carefully re-examined by Stuart and Rush [1954]. These authors formed the opinion that there was actually a good correlation between the brightness fluctuations produced by the photospheric granulation and small-scale variations in velocity, but that this correlation was masked by *large-scale* fluctuations in velocity which did not appear to be closely correlated with brightness. To test this hypothesis they first calculated the coefficient of correlation r between the deviations of velocity and brightness from the overall mean values given by Richardson and Schwarzschild. The resulting value

$$r = -0{\cdot}30$$

indicated only a weak correlation, the negative sign implying that bright areas tend to move upwards and dark areas downwards. Stuart and Rush then used the technique of 'moving-averages' to remove all variations in velocity and brightness on a scale exceeding about 5000 km. Following this they re-computed r in terms of the deviations from the moving-averages, obtaining the value

$$r = -0{\cdot}68.$$

The new figure indicated a strong correlation between velocity and brightness on a scale corresponding to the scale of the granulation pattern, the inferred values of the upward 'granule' velocities being of the order of 0·2 km/sec at the levels of formation of the spectral lines measured.

Independently of Stuart and Rush, Plaskett [1954] also came to the conclusion that the granule velocities were masked by a larger-scale velocity field unrelated to the brightness distribution. This author analysed a number of spectra taken at Oxford and found that the larger-scale field displayed a marked spatial periodicity with a 'wavelength' of about 3500 km and a velocity amplitude of a few tenths of a kilometre per second (see Plaskett's Fig. 5).

Several subsequent investigations into the relationship between brightness and line-of-sight velocity in the photosphere [Servajean, 1961; Bernière, Michard, and Rigal, 1962; Edmonds, 1962a] yielded much smaller (negative) values of the correlation coefficient than the figure of $-0{\cdot}68$ derived by Stuart and Rush, and still left the problem of the true nature of the granule motions unresolved. However, Servajean drew attention to an important fact which served to explain, at least to some extent, the generally low values of the calculated correlation coefficients. He found that, while the brightness and velocity fluctuations were definitely related in the sense that the bright areas were usually associated with upward velocities and the dark areas with downward velocities, there was in fact no proportionality between the *magnitudes* of the brightness fluctuation and the corresponding Doppler shift.

Using spectrograms taken at the Pic-du-Midi, Servajean obtained curves showing the continuum brightness fluctuations and Doppler shifts plotted against distance on the solar surface. These curves were regarded as showing a 'coincidence' whenever a brightness maximum occurred within $0''.6$ of arc of a peak upward velocity or a brightness minimum occurred within $0''.6$ of a peak downward velocity. Conversely, an 'opposition' was said to occur when a brightness maximum coincided within the same accuracy with a peak downward velocity or a brightness minimum with a peak upward velocity. In this way Servajean derived the result

$$\frac{\text{number of 'coincidences'}}{\text{number of 'oppositions'}} = 2{\cdot}75,$$

thus justifying his assertion that the brightness and velocity variations showed a significant correlation in *sense*, though not in numerical magnitude. Shortly afterwards, a somewhat similar result was obtained by Edmonds [1962a: cf. Table 7] from a McMath–Hulbert spectrogram, while Evans and Michard [1962b], using spectra taken at the Sacramento Peak Observatory, concluded that about 70 per cent of bright features in the continuum are associated with violet Doppler shifts and, conversely, about 70 per cent of the dark features show red shifts. This correlation provides powerful evidence for the view that the photospheric granulation is a convective phenomenon (cf. Section 4.5.1).

A new and more powerful attack on the problem of granule velocities was initiated in 1960 when R. B. Leighton, working at the Mt Wilson Observatory, developed an ingenious new technique for 'photographing' line-of-sight velocities with the aid of an ordinary spectroheliograph over the whole, or any selected portion, of the solar disk. Using the new method Leighton and his collaborators immediately established that the velocity field in the upper layers of the photosphere actually consists of two physically distinct regimes: one is a small-scale field of upward and downward vertical motions related in some way to the photospheric granulation, and the other is a large-scale pattern of horizontal motions constituting the phenomenon of the 'supergranulation' described in the next chapter (Section 3.4).

The spectroheliographic method is especially adapted to the task of studying temporal changes in velocity fields and was used by Leighton, Noyes, and Simon [1962] to make the first systematic study of the *time* variation of the small-scale photospheric velocity field. This led them to the striking discovery that the small-scale field is *oscillatory* in character, the pattern of velocities varying almost sinusoidally in time with a period very close to 5 min. Confirmation of the discovery was quickly afforded by observations made by Evans and Michard [1962c] and by Howard [1962], using in each case an entirely different observational technique.[9] A graphic illustration of the presence of the oscillatory velocities is provided by a beautiful series of spectrograms published by Evans [1963: Fig. 7].

The existence of the oscillatory velocity field must be regarded as one of the basic dynamical properties of the solar atmosphere and a detailed knowledge of its structure and properties is an essential prerequisite to an understanding of the nature of granule velocities. In the next section, therefore, we shall turn to a description of the properties of the oscillatory field, postponing further discussion of granule velocities to Section 2.4.3.

2.4.2 THE OSCILLATORY VELOCITY FIELD IN THE UPPER PHOTOSPHERE

In the central region of the solar disk the oscillatory velocity field discovered by Leighton presents the appearance of a pattern of upward and downward vertical velocities on a scale roughly comparable to that of the photospheric granulation. At any given point, the velocity displays a striking time periodicity, varying in an almost sinusoidal fashion with a period close to 5 min. Thanks to the efforts of a number of American and French workers we now have quite a detailed knowledge of the properties of the oscillatory velocity field, which may be conveniently summarized under the following headings:

(1) *Periodicity of the velocity pattern.* The method normally used to demonstrate the existence of the periodicity is to evaluate the time autocorrelation function of the velocity field [Evans, Main, Michard, and Servajean, 1962; Evans and Michard, 1962c; Howard, 1962; Leighton, Noyes, and Simon, 1962]. It is true, of course, that the autocorrelation technique is rather a crude tool, since it ignores any possible dispersion in the amplitudes and periods of the individual oscillating elements. Nevertheless, it does enable an estimate of the period to be obtained with an amount of labour much less than that required to determine the time variation of the velocity at a large number of separate points in the velocity field. If $v(\mathbf{r},t)$ is the line-of-sight component of the velocity at a point $\mathbf{r}$ at time t, then the normalized time autocorrelation function averaged over an area S of the solar surface is defined as the quantity

$$\rho(\Delta t) = \frac{\iint v(\mathbf{r},t)\,.\,v(\mathbf{r},t+\Delta t)\,\mathrm{d}S}{\iint [v(\mathbf{r},t)]^2\,\mathrm{d}S}. \tag{2.1}$$

As an example, Fig. 2.2 shows the result of the determination of $\rho(\Delta t)$ made by Howard [1962] using the Babcock magnetograph at the Mt Wilson Observatory, set to record line-of-sight velocities. It is evident that the

[9] Historically, it is interesting to note that long before Leighton's discovery, theoreticians recognized the possibility that the granulation might generate vertical oscillations in the solar atmosphere [cf. Whitney, 1958].

autocorrelation function approximates very closely to a damped sinusoidal curve which, following Leighton [1963], may be well represented by the analytical expression

$$\rho(\Delta t) = e^{-\Delta t/342} \cos\left(2\pi \frac{\Delta t}{300}\right), \tag{2.2}$$

the period of oscillation being 300 sec.

Table 2.6 summarizes the results of the various determinations of the period of oscillation of the velocity field made by means of the autocorrelation technique. Considering the variety of observational methods employed by

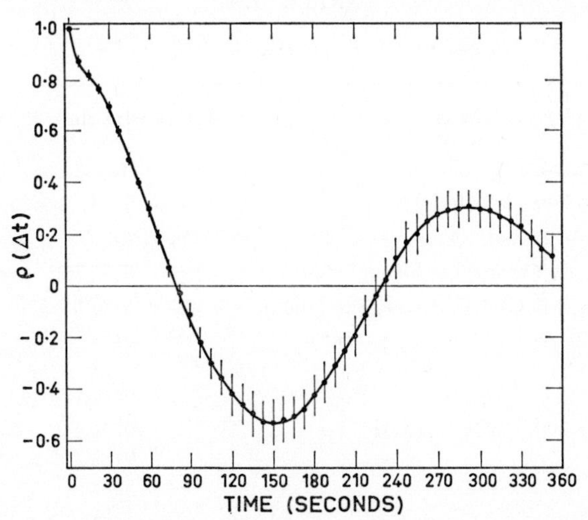

Fig. 2.2. Time autocorrelation function of the small-scale oscillatory velocity field determined by Howard [1962]. It is evident that the autocorrelation function approximates very closely a damped sinusoidal curve with a period of nearly 300 seconds.

the different investigators, the overall agreement is very satisfactory. If we exclude for the moment the values derived from the three *strong* lines Ba II 4554, Na I 5896, and Mg I 5173, we find that the remaining results yield a mean value of 296 sec for the period of the velocity field at the levels of the photosphere where the weaker lines are formed. On the other hand, in the case of the three strong lines, which are formed at higher levels in the atmosphere, the figures obtained by Noyes and Leighton are significantly smaller than 296 sec, suggesting that the period may decrease with height.

(2) *Scale of the velocity pattern.* The question of the spatial scale of the velocity pattern is one of considerable interest because of its bearing on the problem of the relationship between the velocity field and the photospheric granulation. However, the existing observational data essentially take the form of rather crude estimates of the 'sizes' of the individual velocity elements. Evans and Michard [1962c] find the typical size to lie between 2000 and 3000 km, while Leighton, Noyes, and Simon [1962] conclude that the average

size increases from ~1700 to ~3500 km between the levels of formation of the weak Fe 6102 and strong Na 5896 lines. These figures may be compared with the value of 1100 km quoted in Section 2.2.2 as a representative figure for the granule diameter determined from direct photographs, uncorrected for instrumental profile. In contradiction to Leighton *et al.*, Bernière, Michard, and Rigal [1962] find that the increase in the scale of the velocity fluctuations with height is too small to be detected from observations made in lines of different strengths.

TABLE 2.6

Periodicity of the Oscillatory Velocity Field

REFERENCE	SPECTRAL LINE	PERIOD (sec)
Evans and Michard [1962c]	Ti I 5174	~300
Howard [1962]	Fe I 5250	296
Leighton, Noyes, and Simon [1962]	Ca I 6103	296
Evans, Michard, and Servajean [1963]	Ti I 5174	
	Mg I 5173	295
	Fe I 5172	
	Fe I 8514	
Noyes and Leighton [1963]	Fe I 6102	289
	Ca I 6103	296
	Mg I 5528	303
	Ba II 4554	288
	Na I 5896	286
	Mg I 5173	285
Orrall [1965]	Fe I 3931	~295

Unfortunately, the 'size' of a velocity element – like the 'diameter' of a photospheric granule – is necessarily a rather imprecise parameter and it is therefore not possible to make an exact comparison of the scales of the velocity and granulation patterns on the basis of the existing data. Moreover, it must not be forgotten that the effects of seeing, which are generally more serious in spectroscopic work than in direct photography, tend to smear out the individual velocity elements and hence to exaggerate their dimensions. Nevertheless, the weight of the present evidence does suggest that the scale of the velocity pattern, while roughly comparable to that of the granulation, is systematically *somewhat larger*. This matter clearly merits more precise treatment in future observations of the small-scale photospheric velocity field.

(3) *R.m.s. velocity fluctuations.* Detailed measurements of the r.m.s. velocity variations in the central region of the solar disk have been made by Evans

and Michard [1962a] and by Leighton, Noyes, and Simon [1962], as well as by many other workers [see, for example, Goldberg and Pierce, 1959; Goldberg, Mohler, Unno, and Brown, 1960; Servajean, 1961; Bernière, Michard, and Rigal, 1962; Edmonds, 1962a]. The extensive results obtained by Evans and Michard are summarized in their Table 2, which gives the r.m.s. velocity variations derived from measurements of nineteen Fraunhofer lines ranging in Rowland intensity from 0 to 1000. In the case of the twelve weak or medium-strength lines of intensity less than 10, the r.m.s. velocity figures are remarkably concordant, ranging from 0·21 to 0·28 km/sec, with a mean of 0·24 km/sec.[10] The values for the stronger lines are systematically larger and thus indicate an increase in the r.m.s. velocity fluctuation with height.

It must be pointed out that, as in the rather analogous case of the r.m.s. brightness fluctuation in the photospheric granulation pattern (Section 2.2.6), the measured r.m.s. velocity fluctuations do not represent the *actual velocities* of the individual moving elements but give, at best, only some rough indication of their order of magnitude. The true values of the velocity *amplitudes* are discussed below.

(4) *Properties of the individual oscillating elements.* Evans and Michard [1962c] have made a systematic study of the properties of the individual oscillating elements. For this purpose they used a sequence of fifteen good-quality spectrograms covering a period of 500 sec taken at the Sacramento Peak Observatory. From these, curves were plotted showing the time variation of the line-of-sight component of the velocity, $v(\mathbf{r},t)$, at 160 different points along the spectrograph slit. 120 of the points were regularly spaced 1000 km apart, while the remaining forty were selected at positions where pronounced velocity maxima were observed at some time during the 500 sec of observation. The principal spectral lines employed were the weak Ti I 5173·8 and the strong Mg b_2 lines. Similar $v(\mathbf{r},t)$ curves have since been plotted by Jensen and Orrall [1963] and Orrall [1965] from observations made in two weak lines of Fe I.

Figure 2.3 shows some of the $v(\mathbf{r},t)$ curves obtained by Evans and Michard: Fig. 2.3(a) gives the curves at fifteen successive points 1000 km apart derived from the b_2 line, while Fig. 2.3(b) gives the curves at seven widely-spaced points derived from the b_2 line (solid curves) and from the Ti 5173·8 line (dashed curves). The most conspicuous feature of the curves is, of course, the predominantly oscillatory character of the small-scale photospheric velocities. However, it is also evident that the motions in the two lines studied are closely correlated; this conforms with results obtained by the same authors in their [1962a] paper, where they made a detailed study of the correlation between the Doppler displacements in pairs of lines of different intensities. Lines of similar strength show almost identical displacements,

[10] It should be noted that Evans and Michard's results are expressed in terms of a parameter ξ defined as $\sqrt{2} \times$ r.m.s. velocity fluctuation.

but the correspondence gradually diminishes as the intensity difference increases [Evans and Michard, 1962a: cf. Table 4]. However, this effect becomes important only in the case of strong lines formed in the chromosphere.

The presence of vertical oscillatory motions in the upper photosphere raises the interesting question of whether they represent progressive waves moving vertically upwards with definite phase lags between the velocities at different heights or stationary waves with the same phase at all heights.

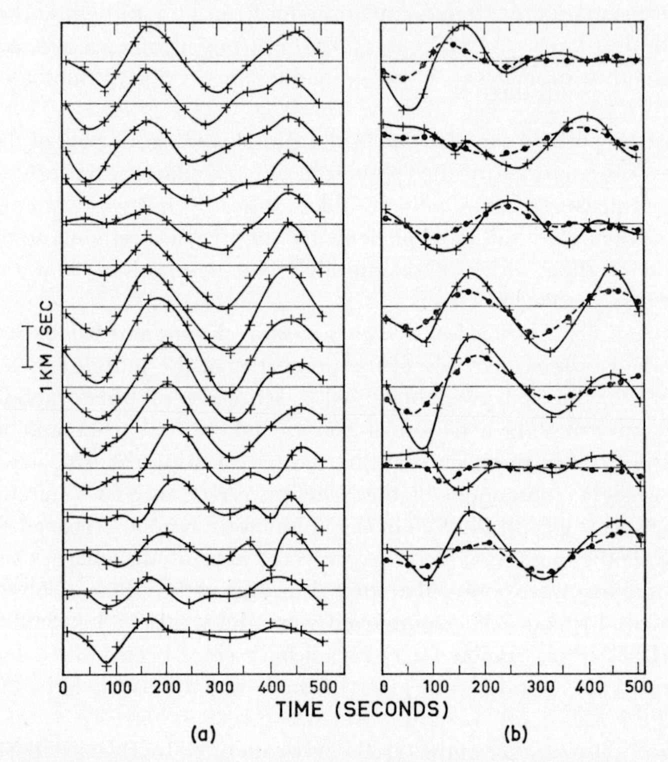

Fig. 2.3. Time variation of the oscillatory velocity field measured by Evans and Michard [1962c].

(*a*) Velocity variation at fifteen successive points 1000 km apart along a line on the solar disk, derived from measurements of Doppler shifts in the Mg b_2 line.

(*b*) Velocity variation at seven widely-spaced points derived from the Mg b_2 line (solid curves) and from the weaker Ti 5173·8 line (dashed curves).

Evans and Michard attempted to resolve this question by estimating the time lag between the motions in the strong Mg b_2 and weak Ti 5173·8 lines at forty-three positions along the slit. They found that at all but three of the points the oscillations in the b_2 line lagged behind those in the Ti line by intervals ranging from 0 to 27 sec, thereby suggesting that the oscillatory motions at different positions represent progressive waves with widely differing velocities. However, perhaps not too much reliance should be placed on this result until independent confirmation is forthcoming. On the one hand, as the reader may judge from Fig. 2.3(*b*), estimates of the time lag between the two velocity curves are very difficult to make while, on the other hand, there is considerable uncertainty regarding the actual geometrical separation between the effective levels of formation of the two lines in question [cf. Athay, 1963].

As one can see from Fig. 2.3, the amplitudes of the individual oscillations are of the order of 0·4 km/sec in the weak Ti 5173·8 line and 0·8 km/sec in the strong Mg b_2 line.[11] Evans and Michard [1962c: cf. Fig. 3] have published histograms showing the distributions of velocity amplitudes in the two lines: these cover the range 0·2 to 0·8 km/sec for the Ti line and 0·4 to 1·4 km/sec for the b_2 line. However, it must be noted that these distributions are truncated at their lower ends since only oscillations with velocity amplitudes greater than 0·4 km/sec in b_2 were selected for measurement. The difference between the amplitudes in the two lines demonstrates once again the existence of a height gradient in the velocity field. This itself introduces a certain degree of ambiguity into the interpretation of the velocity observations. If the line-of-sight velocity were constant throughout the whole depth of line formation, the observed Doppler displacement would correspond to this single velocity value. However, in the presence of a velocity gradient a complex averaging effect must occur, depending on the contribution of each layer to the intensity at each point of the line profile. In general, such a gradient must produce an asymmetrical profile [see also Mein, 1964].

Despite the importance of such information, the only data so far available concerning the lifetime of the oscillating elements of the velocity field is that given by Leighton, Noyes, and Simon [1962]. They find that the quasi-oscillatory motion of the elements may sometimes persist for upwards of three full periods ($\sim$15 min).

According to Evans and Michard [1962c], the line-of-sight oscillatory motions rapidly die away as one moves from the centre towards the limb of the Sun, becoming undetectable at heliocentric angles greater than about 60°. This observation is confirmed by the Doppler photographs of the small-scale field obtained by Leighton, Noyes, and Simon [1962]. It is evident, therefore, that the oscillatory motions occur chiefly in directions at right angles to the Sun's surface.

Finally, to conclude our account of the properties of the oscillatory velocity field in the upper photosphere, we should mention the determination made by Evans and Michard [1962c] of the periods of the oscillating elements directly from the corresponding $v(\mathbf{r},t)$ curves (cf. Fig. 2.3). The mean periods were found to be 249 ± 5 sec in the weak Ti 5173·8 line and 235 ± 4 sec in the strong Mg b_2 line. These figures indicate a decrease in the

[11] The ratio of these amplitudes is consistent with the ratio of the r.m.s. velocities found by Evans and Michard [1962a: Table 2] for the same two lines.

period with height, in qualitative agreement with the conclusion reached by Noyes and Leighton [1963] from their autocorrelation analysis of the velocity pattern as a whole (see Table 2.6 above). Combining the results for the two lines, Evans and Michard found that the periods of the individual oscillations range from 180 to 320 sec but are strongly concentrated around a mean value of 242 sec; the periods are independent of the amplitudes of the oscillations [see also Orrall, 1965]. However, the mean value of 242 sec is considerably less than the figure of 296 sec deduced from autocorrelation analyses of the velocity pattern as a whole (see Table 2.6). Subsequently, Jensen and Orrall [1963] obtained the figure of 273 ± 56 sec for the average period of well-defined oscillations observed in the weak Fe I 3931·1 and 3937·3 lines. This value is higher than that found by Evans and Michard, but is nevertheless below the figure of about 295 sec derived by Orrall [1965] from the same data by an autocorrelation analysis. On the other hand, Zirker [1964] at the Sacramento Peak Observatory has obtained a figure of 290 sec for the mean period of twenty-one 'prominent' oscillations observed in the Fe I 5328·5 line, thus throwing some doubt on the smaller values for the periods obtained by Evans and Michard.

In seeking the cause of these apparent discrepancies one must remember that the 'period' derived from the autocorrelation function is by no means necessarily identical with the dominant period of the individual oscillating elements. In fact, it is easily seen from equation (2.1) that in general this is the case only if we are dealing with an ensemble of damped harmonic oscillations of a single unique frequency, whereas Evans and Michard's results show that there is actually a wide dispersion in the periods of the individual oscillations. This dispersion is hardly surprising in view of the diversity in size, shape, and brightness shown by individual photospheric granules (Sections 2.2.1 and 2.2.4).

2.4.3 RELATIONSHIP BETWEEN THE OSCILLATORY VELOCITY FIELD AND GRANULE MOTIONS

In the preceding section we have outlined the existing observational knowledge of the structure, magnitude, and time variation of the small-scale photospheric velocity field. It remains now to consider to what extent, if any, the observed velocities represent the actual motions of the photospheric granules.

In discussing this problem we must remember that the spectral lines employed in velocity measurements originate at higher levels in the photosphere than the continuous radiation used to obtain direct photographs of the granulation in the central region of the disk. Figure 2.4 is a reproduction of a diagram prepared by Edmonds [1962a] showing the contribution curves for a number of lines typical of those used in measuring photospheric velocities and, in addition, the contribution curve for the continuum at $\lambda 5000$. One can see that the separation between the peaks of the line contribution curves and that of the continuum curve is of the order of 100–200 km. In every case, the amount of overlap between the two curves is relatively small. On the other hand, as we have already emphasized in Section 2.3, the fact that the granulation pattern remains visible up to 5″ of arc from the limb (and possibly even closer) demonstrates that individual granules must persist as coherent structures at least up to an optical depth of 0·1. There is no *a priori* reason, therefore, why the observed small-scale photospheric velocities should not at least partly reflect the actual motions of the granules.

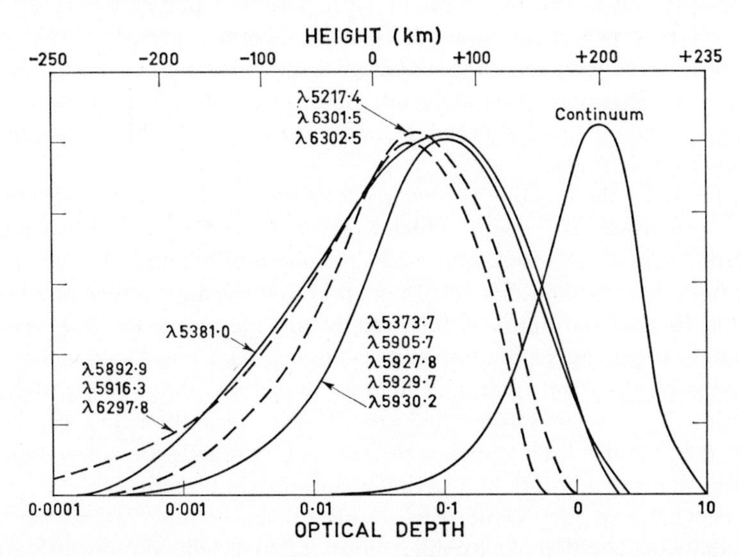

Fig. 2.4. Contribution curves computed by Edmonds [1962a] for the continuum (λ5000) and for a number of spectral lines typical of those used in measuring small-scale photospheric velocities. The height separation between the peaks of the line contribution curves and the maximum of the continuum curve is of the order of 100–200 km.

At first sight, the observational evidence bearing on this question (cf. Sections 2.4.1 and 2.4.2) may seem to be ambiguous, perhaps even somewhat contradictory. On the one hand, good-quality spectrograms of the photospheric granulation indicate that the majority of the bright features in the continuum are associated with upward velocities and the majority of dark features with downward velocities. These facts are well illustrated in Plate 2.4, which shows part of a very good-quality spectrogram obtained recently by J. W. Evans at the Sacramento Peak Observatory under conditions of excellent seeing. The upper photograph (Plate 2.4(*a*)) has been printed to bring up the detail in the continuum and the lower (Plate 2.4(*b*)) to show the structure in the cores of the lines. The four prominent Fraunhofer lines visible are those of Fe I (Nd II) 5191·5, Fe I 5192·4, Ti I 5193·0, and Fe I 5195·0, whose Rowland intensities are 4, 5, 2, and 4 respectively. The letters α, β, γ, and δ on the right-hand side of Plate 2.4(*a*) mark the positions of four of the more prominent granular bright streaks. While there is no indication of any Doppler shift in the lines at the position α, there is a small violet shift at β, only just perceptible on the original photograph, and large violet shifts at γ and δ. Likewise, cases of dark streaks associated with red shifts are readily apparent on a careful scrutiny of the spectrogram.

On the other hand, there is no similarity between the *time* variations in velocity and continuum brightness. The velocity fluctuations are predominantly oscillatory in character with periods lying in the range 4–5 min and may persist for upwards of three complete periods ($\sim$15 min). However, as we have seen in Section 2.2.8, the brightness of most granules appears to remain remarkably constant during the greater part of their lives ($\sim$10 min): there is certainly no kind of periodic fluctuation in the continuum brightness.[12]

Fortunately, there is one further piece of observational evidence, due to Evans and Michard [1962c], which appears to have a crucial bearing on the problem of the relationship between the photospheric granulation and the oscillatory velocity field. These authors find that the appearance of a bright granule in the continuum is followed by the development of a velocity oscillation in the upper photosphere, beginning with an *upward* movement. The velocity rises to its first, and highest, maximum about 40 sec after the granule attains its peak brightness; the velocity oscillation then continues, while the granule itself appears to fade out gradually in a few minutes without showing any sign of a periodic variation in intensity.

Accepted at its face value, Evans and Michard's observation offers an immediate explanation of why the majority of the bright continuum features recorded on isolated spectrograms are associated with upward velocities, while the corresponding actual values of brightness and velocity show little apparent correlation. However, if the mode of granule evolution described in Section 2.2.8 is correct, it would seem that the granules observed by Evans and Michard showed atypical behaviour: direct photographs having a spatial resolution comparable to that of the velocity observations indicate that the majority of granules show little or no change in brightness over most of their lives. In taking a time sequence of spectrograms it is of course extremely difficult to keep the spectrograph slit precisely positioned on individual granules, which tend to undergo continual random displacements in the image plane due to seeing and telescope guiding errors. Consequently, one

[12] The question of whether, at a given point on the Sun, there exists any relationship between the *central intensity* of a Fraunhofer line and the corresponding Doppler shift has been considered by a number of workers [Evans, Michard, and Servajean, 1963; Jensen and Orrall, 1963; Noyes and Leighton, 1963], but the results are rather inconclusive and even somewhat contradictory. Equally perplexing is the relationship between the brightness structure in the centres of Fraunhofer lines of various strengths and the intensity variations in the continuum [see, for example, Evans and Michard, 1962b; Edmonds, 1964; Evans, 1964; Edmonds, Michard, and Servajean, 1965].

must not overlook the possibility of some spurious trend being present in the observations. There is evidently a great need for further observations of the relationship between individual granules and velocity regions during the course of their lives.

In recent years theoreticians have also devoted increasing attention to the problem of photospheric motions, with particular reference to their possible effects on the overlying chromosphere and corona [for references, see Moore and Spiegel, 1964]. Taken in conjunction with modern observational knowledge, this work has led to a more or less generally accepted picture of the basic physical mechanism, which may be briefly summarized as follows: above the granulation visible in the continuum around optical depth $\tau \simeq 1$ there exists a comparatively thin, *but convectively stable*, zone extending up into the lower chromosphere (see Section 4.3.2). This region is continually buffeted by hot, rising convection currents which, as limb observations indicate, penetrate into it up to heights around $\tau \simeq 0 \cdot 1$ (Section 2.3). The ascending granules act like pistons and excite oscillations, perhaps of the resonance type, in the upper photosphere with periods close to 5 min. Although conclusive observational confirmation is still lacking (cf. Section 2.4.2), the oscillations so generated are believed to propagate upwards into the overlying atmosphere and thus provide a mechanism for transporting energy from the convection zone up into the chromosphere and beyond. However, the general problem of the heating and structure of the chromosphere and corona lies beyond the scope of this book.[13]

2.4.4 GRANULE MAGNETIC FIELDS

Routine magnetograms taken with low spatial resolution reveal the existence in the photosphere of weak, large-scale magnetic fields covering substantial areas of the solar disk; these are frequently present even in quiet regions showing no other sign of activity [see, for example, Beggs and von Klüber, 1964; Bumba and Howard, 1965; Leighton, 1965]. The stronger fields associated with activity centres are known to show a fine structure with a scale of about 2″ of arc [Severny, 1959], and one may therefore ask whether the weak fields outside activity regions show a similar fine structure. And, if so, is the fine structure related in any way to the photospheric granulation?

These questions were investigated by Steshenko [1960] using observations made with the large spectrograph of the solar tower at the Crimean Astrophysical Observatory, equipped with a polarizing device for the measurement of longitudinal magnetic fields. The precision of the measurements was limited by air turbulence in the spectrograph, which caused the spectral lines to move in a random, zigzag manner by amounts corresponding to

[13] For detailed discussions of these topics the interested reader is referred to the review articles by van de Hulst [1953], Pagel [1964], and Kuperus [1965].

Zeeman shifts of up to ± 23 gauss. Nevertheless, Steshenko succeeded in placing an upper limit of about 50 gauss on the strength of any longitudinal field possibly associated with individual granules. On the other hand, he found that groups of granules coinciding with the regions of highest upward velocity were associated with longitudinal fields of the order of 50–60 gauss.

Subsequently Semel [1962], analysing spectroscopic observations obtained by R. Michard at the Sacramento Peak Observatory, also found some evidence for the existence of a fine structure in the weak magnetic fields outside activity regions. However, a qualitative examination of the records gave no indication of any strong correlation between the field distribution and the granulation pattern; the mean field strength was about 24 gauss. Finally, Howard [1962] made magnetic tracings using the magnetograph at the Mt Wilson Observatory with an aperture 2″ of arc in diameter – roughly the size of a large granule – and obtained an upper limit of $8{\cdot}2 \pm 4{\cdot}4$ gauss for the r.m.s. variation of the longitudinal component of the field in undisturbed regions of the Sun. Howard found no indication in the magnetic records of any oscillatory fluctuations of the type displayed by the small-scale velocity field in the upper photosphere.

On the basis of the available observational data we must conclude that there is as yet no reliable evidence for the existence of magnetic fields associated with individual photospheric granules. Moreover, even if such fields do exist, their strengths cannot exceed a few tens of gauss at the very most; fields of this magnitude would in any case be very unlikely to influence the dynamics of the individual granules.

Much stronger fields, of the order of 100–200 gauss, are known to occur in the immediate vicinity of sunspots, and one may ask whether these fields have any effect on the granulation. Observations bearing on this question have been fully described in the authors' monograph on sunspots [Bray and Loughhead, 1964: Section 3.3.2] and here we need only state the main conclusion: apart from what appear to be fairly rare, exceptional cases, the appearance, diameter, separation, and lifetime of the granules remain unaltered right up to the immediate boundaries of the spots.

In contrast to the generally unaltered appearance of the granulation in the neighbourhood of well-established sunspots, cases of a definite disturbance have been observed by the authors and by R. A. Miller in the granulation between new and developing sunspot pores [*loc. cit.*, Section 3.3.4]. The disturbance takes the form of a number of dark lanes running roughly parallel to a line joining the pores, which are assumed to be of opposite polarity; it has been interpreted as direct evidence of an interaction between a rising loop of magnetic flux and the photospheric convection currents. Actual magnetic measurements of such disturbances might help to elucidate the rôle played by the granules in convecting internal magnetic fields to the surface, but such observations have not yet been attempted.

TABLE 2.7

High-Resolution Observations of the Photospheric Granulation

REFERENCE	OBSERVATORY	APERTURE (cm)	NATURE OF OBSERVATIONS
Janssen [1896]	Meudon	13·5	Granule diameters
Hansky [1905]	Pulkovo	—	Diameters
Hansky [1908]	Pulkovo	—	Photographs
Chevalier [1908]	Zô-Sè	30	Photographs
Chevalier [1914]	Zô-Sè	36	Diameters
Strebel [1932]	Munich	20	Photographs
Strebel [1933]	Munich	20	Polygonal nature of granules
ten Bruggencate [1938]	Potsdam	10	Photographs
Keenan [1938]	Yerkes	19	Diameters and cell size
Keenan [1939]	Yerkes	19	Photometry
von Klüber and Müller [1948]	Potsdam	10	Photographs
Richardson and Schwarzschild [1950]	Mt Wilson	30	Doppler velocities
Macris [1953]	Pic-du-Midi	23	Lifetimes
McMath, Mohler, and Pierce [1955]	McMath–Hulbert	—	Doppler velocities
McMath, Mohler, Pierce, and Goldberg [1956]	McMath–Hulbert	—	Doppler velocities
Leighton [1957]	Mt Wilson	30	Lifetimes
Rösch [1957]	Pic-du-Midi	23	Diameters; granulation near the extreme limb
Bray and Loughhead [1958b]	Sydney	13	Lifetimes and evolution
Blackwell, Dewhirst, and Dollfus [1959]	Balloon	30	Granular contrast
Bray and Loughhead [1959]	Sydney	13	Cell size
Schwarzschild [1959]	Balloon	30	Polygonal nature of granules
Rösch [1959]	Pic-du-Midi	23	Cell size and photometry
Rösch and Hugon [1959]	Pic-du-Midi	23; 38	Lifetimes and evolution
Loughhead and Bray [1960b]	Sydney	13	Granulation near the extreme limb
Miller [1960]	Manila	10	Granule counts in neighbourhood of sunspots
Steshenko [1960]	Crimea	—	Fine structure of photospheric magnetic fields
Bahng and Schwarzschild [1961a]	Balloon	30	Lifetimes
Bahng and Schwarzschild [1961b]	Balloon	30	R.m.s. brightness variation
Loughhead and Bray [1961]	Sydney	13	Disturbances in granulation near growing sunspot pores
Macris and Banos [1961]	Athens	30	Cell size
Evans and Michard [1962c]	Sacramento Peak	30	Oscillatory velocities
Leighton, Noyes, and Simon [1962]	Mt Wilson	30	Oscillatory velocities
Macris and Prokakis [1962]	Athens	40	Granule diameter measurements in neighbourhood of sunspots
Macris and Prokakis [1963]	Athens	30	Lifetimes

2.5 Summary of High-Resolution Observations of the Photospheric Granulation, 1896–1963

In the preceding account of the morphology, evolution, and dynamics of the photospheric granulation, we have relied almost exclusively on modern observations, the earlier photographic and visual observations having been dealt with in Chapter 1, largely from a historical point of view. However, in order to give a bird's-eye view of all important contributions, we have summarized in Table 2.7 successful observations of the granulation made from 1896, when Janssen published the first good photographs, to 1963. The table gives the source reference, the location and aperture of the telescope employed, and the nature of the investigation. Observations are included only when there is clear evidence in the published paper that a resolution of 1–2″ of arc was actually achieved. Purely visual observations are excluded, as are re-discussions of existing observations. It is rather disappointing to note the absence of any significant new observations from 1963 to the time of writing (February, 1966), although a number of discussions of existing data have appeared during this period.

REFERENCES

ATHAY, R. G. [1963] 'Depth of formation of Mg I lines in the solar atmosphere', *Astrophys. J.* **138,** 680.

BAHNG, J. D. R., and SCHWARZSCHILD, M. [1961a] 'Lifetime of solar granules', *Astrophys. J.* **134,** 312.

BAHNG, J. D. R., and SCHWARZSCHILD, M. [1961b] 'The temperature fluctuations in the solar granulation', *Astrophys. J.* **134,** 337.

BEGGS, D. W., and KLÜBER, H. VON [1964] 'Measurements of the general magnetic field of the Sun with a magnetograph', *Mon. Not. R.A.S.* **127,** 133.

BERNIÈRE, G., MICHARD, R., and RIGAL, G. [1962] 'Étude statistique des fluctuations locales de brillance et de vitesse dans la photosphère', *Ann. Astrophys.* **25,** 279.

BLACKWELL, D. E., DEWHIRST, D. W., and DOLLFUS, A. [1959] 'The observation of solar granulation from a manned balloon. I. Observational data and measurement of contrast', *Mon. Not. R.A.S.* **119,** 98.

BRAY, R. J., and LOUGHHEAD, R. E. [1958a] 'The lifetime of sunspot penumbra filaments', *Aust. J. Phys.* **11,** 185.

BRAY, R. J., and LOUGHHEAD, R. E. [1958b] 'Observations of changes in the photospheric granules', *Aust. J. Phys.* **11,** 507.

BRAY, R. J., and LOUGHHEAD, R. E. [1959] 'High resolution observations of the granular structure of sunspot umbrae', *Aust. J. Phys.* **12,** 320.

BRAY, R. J., and LOUGHHEAD, R. E. [1961] 'Facular granule lifetimes determined with a seeing-monitored photoheliograph', *Aust. J. Phys.* **14,** 14.

BRAY, R. J., and LOUGHHEAD, R. E. [1964] *Sunspots*. (Chapman and Hall: London).

BRUGGENCATE, P. TEN [1938] 'Beitrag zur Technik von Granulationsaufnahmen', *Z. Astrophys.* **16,** 374.

BRUGGENCATE, P. TEN, and GROTRIAN, W. [1936] 'Die Bestimmung der mittleren Lebensdauer der Granulation', *Z. Astrophys.* **12,** 323.

BUMBA, V., and HOWARD, R. [1965] 'Large-scale distribution of solar magnetic fields', *Astrophys. J.* **141,** 1502.

CHEVALIER, S. [1908] 'Contribution to the study of the photosphere', *Astrophys. J.* **27,** 12.

CHEVALIER, S. [1914] 'Étude photographique de la photosphère solaire', *Ann. Obs. Zô-Sè* **8,** C1.

EDMONDS, F. N. [1960] 'On solar granulation', *Astrophys. J.* **131,** 57.

EDMONDS, F. N. [1962a] 'A coherence analysis of Fraunhofer line fine structure and continuum brightness fluctuations near the center of the solar disk', *Astrophys. J.* **136,** 507.

EDMONDS, F. N. [1962b] 'A statistical photometric analysis of granulation across the solar disk', *Astrophys. J. Suppl.* **6,** 357.

EDMONDS, F. N. [1964] 'Statistical analysis of photospheric inhomogeneities in spectrograms', *Trans. I.A.U.* **12B,** 166.

EDMONDS, F. N., MICHARD, R., and SERVAJEAN, R. [1965] 'Observational studies of macroscopic inhomogeneities in the solar atmosphere. VII. A statistical analysis of photometric and kinematic inhomogeneities in the deep photosphere', *Ann. Astrophys.* **28,** 534.

EVANS, J. W. [1963] 'Motions in the solar atmosphere', *Sky and Tel.* **25,** 321.

EVANS, J. W. [1964] 'Inclined inhomogeneities in the solar photosphere', *Astrophysica Norvegica* **9,** 33.

EVANS, J. W., MAIN, P., MICHARD, R., and SERVAJEAN, R. [1962] 'Correlations in the time variations of macroscopic inhomogeneities in the solar atmosphere', *Astrophys. J.* **136,** 682.

EVANS, J. W., and MICHARD, R. [1962a] 'Observational study of macroscopic inhomogeneities in the solar atmosphere. I. Velocity displacements of Fraunhofer lines as a function of line strength and position on disk', *Astrophys. J.* **135,** 812.

EVANS, J. W., and MICHARD, R. [1962b] 'Observational study of macroscopic inhomogeneities in the solar atmosphere. II. Brightness fluctuations in Fraunhofer lines and the continuum', *Astrophys. J.* **136,** 487.

EVANS, J. W., and MICHARD, R. [1962c] 'Observational study of macroscopic inhomogeneities in the solar atmosphere. III. Vertical oscillatory motions in the solar photosphere', *Astrophys. J.* **136,** 493.

EVANS, J. W., MICHARD, R., and SERVAJEAN, R. [1963] 'Observational study of macroscopic inhomogeneities in the solar atmosphere. V. Statistical study of the time variations of solar inhomogeneities', *Ann. Astrophys.* **26,** 368.

GIOVANELLI, R. G. [1961] 'On the centre-limb variation of granule contrast', *Mon. Not. R.A.S.* **122,** 523.

GOLDBERG, L., MOHLER, O. C., UNNO, W., and BROWN, J. [1960] 'The measurement of the local Doppler shift of Fraunhofer lines', *Astrophys. J.* **132,** 184.

GOLDBERG, L., and PIERCE, A. K. [1959] 'The photosphere of the Sun'. (*Handbuch der Physik,* ed. S. FLÜGGE, vol. 52, p. 1; Springer: Berlin).

HANSKY, A. [1905] 'Photographies de la granulation solaire faites à Poulkovo', *Pulkovo Mitt.* **1,** 81.

HANSKY, A. [1908] 'Mouvement des granules sur la surface du Soleil', *Pulkovo Mitt.* **3,** 1.

HARVEY, J. W., and RAMSEY, H. E. [1963] 'Photospheric granulation in the near ultraviolet', *Publ. Astron. Soc. Pac.* **75,** 283.

HOWARD, R. [1962] 'Preliminary solar magnetograph observations with small apertures', *Astrophys. J.* **136,** 211.

HULST, H. C. VAN DE [1953] 'The chromosphere and the corona'. (*The Sun,* ed. G. KUIPER, p. 207; Univ. Chicago Press).

JAGER, C. DE [1959] 'Structure and dynamics of the solar atmosphere'. (*Handbuch der Physik,* ed. S. FLÜGGE, vol. 52, p. 80; Springer: Berlin).

JANSSEN, J. [1896] 'Étude de la surface solaire par la photographie', *Ann. Obs. Meudon* **1,** 103.

JENSEN, E., and ORRALL, F. Q. [1963] 'Observational study of macroscopic inhomogeneities in the solar atmosphere. IV. Velocity and intensity fluctuations observed in the K line', *Astrophys. J.* **138,** 252.

KEENAN, P. C. [1938] 'Dimensions of the solar granules', *Astrophys. J.* **88,** 360.

KEENAN, P. C. [1939] 'Photometry of the solar granules', *Astrophys. J.* **89,** 604.

KLÜBER, H. VON, and MÜLLER, H. [1948] 'Bemerkungen zur Technik direkter Sonnenaufnahmen mit langbrennweitigen Instrumenten', *Z. Astrophys.* **24,** 207.

KUPERUS, M. [1965] 'The transfer of mechanical energy in the Sun and the heating of the corona', *Recherches Astron. Obs. Utrecht* **17**(1), 1.

LEIGHTON, R. B. [1957] 'Some observations of solar granulation', *Publ. Astron. Soc. Pac.* **69,** 497.

LEIGHTON, R. B. [1963] 'The solar granulation', *Ann. Rev. Astron. Astrophys.* **1,** 19.

LEIGHTON, R. B. [1965] 'Small scale solar magnetic fields, plages, filaments: observations. Introductory report'. (*Stellar and Solar Magnetic Fields,* ed. R. LÜST, p. 158; North-Holland Publ. Co.: Amsterdam).

LEIGHTON, R. B., NOYES, R. W., and SIMON, G. W. [1962] 'Velocity fields in the solar atmosphere. I. Preliminary report', *Astrophys. J.* **135,** 474.

LOUGHHEAD, R. E., and BRAY, R. J. [1960a] 'The lifetime and cell size of the granulation in sunspot umbrae', *Aust. J. Phys.* **13,** 139.

LOUGHHEAD, R. E., and BRAY, R. J. [1960b] 'Granulation near the extreme solar limb', *Aust. J. Phys.* **13,** 738.

LOUGHHEAD, R. E., and BRAY, R. J. [1961] 'Phenomena accompanying the birth of sunspot pores', *Aust. J. Phys.* **14**, 347.

MACRIS, C. [1953] 'Recherches sur la granulation photosphérique', *Ann. Astrophys.* **16**, 19.

MACRIS, C. J., and BANOS, G. J. [1961] 'Mean distance between photospheric granules and its change with the solar activity', *Mem. Nat. Obs. Athens:* Series 1, No. 8.

MACRIS, C., and ELIAS, D. [1955] 'Sur une variation du nombre des granules photosphériques en fonction de l'activité solaire', *Ann. Astrophys.* **18**, 143.

MACRIS, C. J., and PROKAKIS, T. J. [1962] 'Sur une différence des dimensions des granules photosphériques au voisinage et loin de la pénombre des taches solaires', *C.R. Acad. Sci.* **255**, 1862.

MACRIS, C., and PROKAKIS, T. [1963] 'New results on the lifetime of the solar granules', *Mem. Nat. Obs. Athens:* Series 1, No. 10.

MCMATH, R. R., MOHLER, O. C., and PIERCE, A. K. [1955] 'Doppler shifts in solar granules', *Astrophys. J.* **122**, 565.

MCMATH, R. R., MOHLER, O. C., PIERCE, A. K., and GOLDBERG, L. [1956] 'Preliminary results with a vacuum solar spectrograph', *Astrophys. J.* **124**, 1.

MEIN, P. [1964] 'Étude d'une raie solaire perturbée par des ondes acoustiques planes', *C.R. Acad. Sci.* **258**, 453; **258**, 819.

MILLER, R. A. [1960] 'Observations on photospheric brightness surrounding sunspots', *J. Brit. Astron. Assoc.* **70**, 146.

MOORE, D. W., and SPIEGEL, E. A. [1964] 'The generation and propagation of waves in a compressible atmosphere', *Astrophys. J.* **139**, 48.

NOYES, R. W., and LEIGHTON, R. B. [1963] 'Velocity fields in the solar atmosphere. II. The oscillatory field', *Astrophys. J.* **138**, 631.

ORRALL, F. Q. [1965] 'Observational study of macroscopic inhomogeneities in the solar atmosphere. VI. Photospheric oscillations and chromospheric structure', *Astrophys. J.* **141**, 1131.

PAGEL, B. E. J. [1964] 'The structure of the solar chromosphere', *Ann. Rev. Astron. Astrophys.* **2**, 267.

PLASKETT, H. H. [1954] 'Motions in the Sun at the photospheric level. V. Velocities of granules and of other localized regions', *Mon. Not. R.A.S.* **114**, 251.

PLASKETT, H. H. [1955] 'Physical conditions in the solar photosphere'. (*Vistas in Astronomy*, ed. A. BEER, vol. 1, p. 637; Pergamon: London).

RICHARDSON, R. S., and SCHWARZSCHILD, M. [1950] 'On the turbulent velocities of solar granules', *Astrophys. J.* **111**, 351.

RÖSCH, J. [1957] 'Photographies de la photosphère et des taches solaires', *L'Astronomie* **71**, 129.

RÖSCH, J. [1959] 'Observations sur la photosphère solaire. II. Numération et photométrie photographique des granules dans le domaine spectral 5900–6000Å', *Ann. Astrophys.* **22**, 584.

RÖSCH, J. [1960] 'Granulation observations from the Pic-du-Midi'.

(*Aerodynamic Phenomena in Stellar Atmospheres*, ed. R. N. THOMAS, p. 313; I.A.U. Symposium No. 12: *Nuov. Cim. Suppl.* **22,** No. 1).

RÖSCH, J. [1962] 'Results drawn from photographs of the photosphere obtained from the ground', *Trans. I.A.U.* **11B,** 197.

RÖSCH, J., and HUGON, M. [1959] 'Sur l'évolution dans le temps de la granulation photosphérique', *C.R. Acad. Sci.* **249,** 625.

SCHRÖTER, E. H. [1962] 'Einige Beobachtungen und Messungen an Stratoskop I-Negativen', *Z. Astrophys.* **56,** 183.

SCHWARZSCHILD, M. [1959] 'Photographs of the solar granulation taken from the stratosphere', *Astrophys. J.* **130,** 345.

SCHWARZSCHILD, M. [1961] 'Convection in stars', *Astrophys. J.* **134,** 1.

SEMEL, M. [1962] 'Sur la détermination du champ magnétique de la granulation solaire', *C.R. Acad. Sci.* **254,** 3978.

SERVAJEAN, R. [1961] 'Contribution à l'étude de la cinématique de la matière dans les taches et la granulation solaire', *Ann. Astrophys.* **24,** 1.

SEVERNY, A. B. [1959] 'Fine structure of the magnetic field and depolarization of radiation in sunspots', *Astron. J. U.S.S.R.* **36,** 208 (*Sov. Astron. AJ* **3,** 214).

STESHENKO, N. V. [1960] 'On the determination of magnetic fields of solar granulation', *Izv. Crim. Astrophys. Obs.* **22,** 49.

STREBEL, H. [1932] 'Sonnenphotographische Dokumente', *Z. Astrophys.* **5,** 36.

STREBEL, H. [1933] 'Beitrag zum Problem der Sonnengranulation', *Z. Astrophys.* **6,** 313.

STUART, F. E., and RUSH, J. H. [1954] 'Correlation analyses of turbulent velocities and brightness of the photospheric granulation', *Astrophys. J.* **120,** 245.

VOIGT, H. H. (ed.) [1965] *Landolt–Börnstein – Numerical Data and Functional Relationships in Science and Technology*, New Series, Group VI, vol. I: *Astronomy and Astrophysics.* (Springer: Berlin).

WALDMEIER, M. [1940] 'Die Feinstruktur der Sonnenoberfläche', *Helv. Phys. Act.* **13,** 13.

WHITNEY, C. [1958] 'Granulation and oscillations of the solar atmosphere', *Smiths. Contr. Astrophys.* **2,** 365.

ZIRKER, J. B. [1964] 'On the periods of large-amplitude photospheric oscillations', *Ann. Astrophys.* **27,** 429.

CHAPTER 3

Sunspot Umbra Granules, Facular Granules, and the Supergranulation

3.1 Introduction

The photospheric granulation owes its origin to the existence of subphotospheric convection currents which contribute to the outward transport of energy from deeper layers and thus help to maintain the overall energy balance of the Sun. In the neighbourhood of activity centres, however, these convective processes are drastically modified – a fact manifested by the appearance of sunspots and photospheric ('white-light') faculae in these regions. Nevertheless, sunspots themselves show a granular structure in their umbrae, on a scale comparable to that of the photospheric granulation, while the photospheric faculae consist in the main of loose conglomerations of individual facular granules mostly 1–2″ of arc in diameter. Do these sunspot and facular fine structures also owe their origin to the same underlying convective processes responsible for the photospheric granulation? If so, their differences in appearance and properties may well be due, directly or indirectly, to the influence on the convection currents of the magnetic fields which are known to pervade sunspots and faculae. Conversely, a study of the differences between the properties of the photospheric granules and the umbral and facular granules might well throw additional light on the nature of the underlying convective motions and hence on the origin of the photospheric granulation itself. In the present chapter we shall briefly discuss what answers can be given to these questions in the light of existing observational knowledge, dealing first with the umbral granulation (Section 3.2) and then with the photospheric facular granules (Section 3.3).

In 1960 R. B. Leighton, working at the Mt Wilson Observatory, drew attention to the existence in the upper levels of the photosphere of a large-scale and comparatively well-ordered system of horizontal motions whose appearance is highly suggestive of the flow patterns observed in cellular convection. Although the velocities are mainly horizontal and the cell size is much larger than that of the photospheric granulation, the velocity field nevertheless bears a certain resemblance to the ordinary photospheric granulation and was accordingly named by Leighton the 'supergranulation'. Most of the main quantitative parameters pertaining to the supergranulation now seem fairly firmly established; they are summarized in Section 3.4. The supergranulation is believed to owe its origin to a weakly unstable region some thousands of kilometres below the visible photosphere, the instability being due to the de-ionization of singly- or doubly-ionized helium, or perhaps both.

To conclude this chapter, we present in Section 3.5 a table summarizing all the available observational information concerning the properties of the various structures discussed, as well as, for comparison, the corresponding properties of the photospheric granulation.

3.2 Granulation in Sunspot Umbrae

During the past decade the application of special techniques to the photography of the fine structure of sunspot umbrae has demonstrated that an umbral granulation is practically always present, irrespective of the spot's size or stage of development. In all cases that have been adequately observed, the umbral granules form a well-defined cellular pattern which, apart from an obvious difference due to the non-uniform brightness distribution in spot umbrae, resembles the photospheric granulation. The umbral granules are, however, more closely packed than the photospheric granules and their lifetimes are much longer. Nevertheless, the general similarity of the umbral granulation to the photospheric granulation strongly suggests that *it also has a convective origin.* If so, it follows that even the strong magnetic fields present in the umbrae of large spots fail to suppress the convective motions. On the other hand, the influence of the spot magnetic field on the convection currents within the umbra may well be responsible for the smaller cell size actually observed, though it is not clear how the magnetic field would affect the lifetime.

A detailed account of the observed properties of the umbral granulation is to be found in the authors' monograph on sunspots [Bray and Loughhead, 1964: pp. 82–89; see also Plates 3.7(*d*), 3.15–3.19]. More recent observations [Danielson, 1964a,b; Rösch, 1964; Bumba, 1965] have not greatly added to the information contained in this account, which is based largely on the authors' own observations. However, one point of interest is that the value of 1″.5 of arc quoted by Rösch for the mean cell size of the umbral granulation is significantly smaller than the figure of 2″.3 obtained by the authors [*loc. cit.*, pp. 86–87]. It is tempting to speculate that the granule separation in any given region of a spot umbra depends on the local strength and configuration of the magnetic field. However, evidence to support this speculation is entirely lacking at the present time. No measurements of the cell size based on Danielson's photographs, taken from the stratosphere, have yet been published.

3·3 Photospheric Facular Granules

Photospheric ('white-light') faculae are visible only near the limb and, as a rule, are distributed over a large area in the neighbourhood of a sunspot group. No spots near the limb are observed without attendant faculae and, conversely, except for the polar faculae, which occur in zones where spots do not normally appear, there are few faculae which are not associated with spot groups at some stage of their lives [cf. Waldmeier, 1955: p. 200; Bray and Loughhead, 1964: p. 248].

The typical appearance of an extended facular region surrounding a sunspot group near the limb is well illustrated in Plate 3.1, which is a reproduction of a photograph obtained by the authors with the Sydney 5-inch photoheliograph. It is immediately evident from Plate 3.1 that each facular area is composed of a loose conglomeration of individual *bright facular granules* mostly 1–2″ of arc in diameter. The granules are superimposed on a background of normal photospheric brightness; the intensity of the photosphere is not raised in the neighbourhood of faculae, in contradiction to the remarks of ten Bruggencate [1942] and Rogerson [1961]. The existence of the facular granules was first pointed out by two independent observers, ten Bruggencate [1940] and Waldmeier [1940]. Prior to this time it was believed that faculae were devoid of fine structure [cf. Plaskett, 1936]; the same erroneous assumption is unfortunately still implicit in many modern spectrophotometric investigations of faculae.

In most cases the facular granules are not sufficiently compacted to form a pattern; even in big clusters composed of, say, twenty or more individual granules, they are often spread out along intersecting lines. For this reason it is *not* possible to define a mean cell size similar to that measured for the photospheric and umbral granulation (cf. Sections 2.2.3 and 3.2). In any case, not all facular granules occur in clusters: many occur as completely isolated structures, surrounded by photospheric granules of normal brightness. In certain other respects, too, the facular granules differ markedly from the photospheric granules in their properties, which may conveniently be discussed under the following headings:

(1) *Lifetime.* ten Bruggencate [1940] estimated the lifetimes of the individual facular granules to be of the order of one hour, while Waldmeier [1940] found that many facular granules last for more than two hours. These estimates, however, were based simply on comparisons of pairs of photographs taken one hour and two hours apart respectively. Subsequently, a more systematic determination of the lifetimes was made by the present authors [Bray and Loughhead, 1961] using a good-quality sequence covering a period of $5\frac{1}{2}$ hr of the facular region illustrated in Plate 3.1. The results

confirmed the work of ten Bruggencate and Waldmeier in showing that the individual facular granules are much longer-lived than the photospheric granules: some 80 per cent have lifetimes exceeding 1 hr, 50 per cent exceeding 2 hr, 25 per cent exceeding 4 hr, and 10 per cent exceeding 5 hr.

No significant tendency was found for short-lived granules, on the one hand, or long-lived granules, on the other, to cluster together. Isolated facular granules have lifetimes similar to those of members of clusters.

Plate 3.2, which is taken from the authors' paper, illustrates the stability of the facular granules in a small selected region over a period of $5\frac{1}{2}$ hr. Although there are some changes due to the growth of new granules, two persist over the entire sequence; these are located in the lower corners of the photographs.

(2) *Evolution.* So far only one attempt has been made to study the evolution of the individual facular granules [Bray and Loughhead, 1961]. However, unlike the cases of the photospheric and umbral granules, it is hardly possible to make a systematic study of changes in the brightness, size, and shape of individual facular granules during their observed lifetimes. In the first place, since the facular granules are only observable close to the limb, their apparent sizes and shapes depend on the degree of foreshortening which, because of solar rotation, changes during the life of a granule. Secondly, any intrinsic variations in the brightness of a granule are masked by changes due to its varying heliocentric angle. The most that can be said is that no systematic changes in brightness were established; faint granules appear to remain faint throughout their lifetimes and, similarly, bright granules appear to remain bright.

On the other hand, some information was obtained by the authors about the process of growth and decay of individual granules. It was found that a facular granule develops quite suddenly in a region of hitherto normal photospheric brightness, being preceded – at least occasionally – by a patch of diffuse material of intermediate brightness some 3–4″ of arc in diameter. The transition from a region of normal photospheric brightness to a recognizable facular granule takes place in a period short compared with the average lifetime. A facular granule appears to lose its identity either by fading and being replaced by material of photospheric brightness, or by coalescing with another granule. The final fading takes place in a time short compared with the lifetime. In two cases an interesting variant was noticed: the original granule disappeared and was replaced by two facular granules on either side of its former position. These in turn were quickly replaced by ordinary photospheric material.

(3) *Granules near the extreme solar limb.* An examination of a large number of limb films taken with the Sydney 5-inch photoheliograph has revealed that individual facular granules are often clearly visible only 1–2″ of arc from the limb [Bray and Loughhead, 1961]. By comparison, the photospheric

granules have not yet been distinguished closer than 4″ to the limb (Section 2.3). This may be evidence that the facular granules extend up to a greater height than the photospheric granules, although it should be pointed out that the failure to detect photospheric granules closer to the limb may be solely an observational effect resulting from their lower contrast. The fact that the facular granules are invisible at the centre of the disk, i.e. that their contrast *increases* with heliocentric angle θ up to a certain value of θ, also implies a greater height [cf. Waldmeier, 1955: p. 208].

In the light of the information summarized above, it is clear that apart from their greater brightness, the facular granules differ from the photospheric granules in at least two important respects. Firstly, in most cases the facular granules are not sufficiently compacted to form a well-defined cellular pattern. Secondly, their lifetimes are an order of magnitude greater than those of the photospheric granules. Hence, in spite of a superficial resemblance, it is likely that the two types of granules owe their origins to different physical mechanisms.[1]

As ten Bruggencate pointed out, a remarkable feature of the facular granules is the extraordinary stability shown by the individual granules: a single granule, only 750–1500 km in diameter, can persist as an isolated structure – in some cases well removed from sunspots and neighbouring faculae – for a period of several hours. It is tempting to speculate that both the enhanced emission and the stability are due in some way to the influence of the magnetic field known to pervade facular regions. If so, the observations imply that the influence of the field is sometimes concentrated within regions no larger, and possibly much smaller, than a single facular granule.

3·4 The Supergranulation

The existence of a large-scale system of horizontal velocities in the upper levels of the photosphere was first discovered by Hart [1954, 1956] at Oxford in the course of a new determination of the Sun's rotational velocity, undertaken with a view to elucidating the origin of certain discrepancies among the results of earlier determinations. She found that the individual motions occurred on an irregular scale ranging from about 25,000 to 85,000 km and persisted for at least several hours; the velocities involved were as high as 0·5 km/sec. However, it was not until 1960, when R. B. Leighton at the

[1] Rogerson [1961] has formulated a facular model based on the assumption that the facular granules are to be identified with the brighter photospheric granules seen at the centre of the disk. However, in proposing his model Rogerson has evidently overlooked the order of magnitude difference in the lifetimes.

Mt Wilson Observatory pioneered his new spectroheliographic technique of 'photographing' solar velocities (cf. Section 2.4.1), that the true extent and significance of the horizontal motions were fully realized. Since then, thanks to the continued efforts of Leighton and his collaborators [Leighton, Noyes, and Simon, 1962; Leighton, 1963; Simon, 1964; Simon and Leighton, 1964], quite a detailed picture has been built up both of the structure and properties of the horizontal velocity field and of its relationship to other solar phenomena.

The extent and regularity of the system of horizontal motions is immediately apparent from Plate 3.3. This is a typical Doppler photograph of the Sun, taken in the line Ca I 6103, in which line-of-sight velocities appear as light or dark shading according as to whether they are directed towards or away from the observer and in which the effect of solar rotation has been largely removed. It is evident that the velocity field is made up of numerous velocity 'cells', each many thousands of kilometres in diameter, standing out against a grey (stationary) background. Near the limb the cells show evidence of geometrical foreshortening. Near the centre of the disk they are hardly visible at all, thus indicating that the velocities are predominantly horizontal. There is no detectable difference in the appearance of the velocity pattern between equatorial and polar regions, but it is more difficult to study at latitudes exceeding $\pm 60°$ [Leighton, Noyes, and Simon, 1962].

Most of the individual velocity cells visible on Plate 3.3 display one remarkable regularity: the line-of-sight velocity is directed towards the observer on the side of the cell facing towards the centre of the disk and away from the observer on the side facing the limb. This is manifested by the fact that the cells appear bright on the centre side and dark on the limb side. This observation may be interpreted as implying that the motion in each cell is directed outwards from the centre towards the boundary. More recently, Lévy [1965] has drawn the same conclusion from spectroheliographic observations obtained at the Meudon Observatory.

In their [1962] paper Leighton and his co-workers pointed out that the horizontal velocity field bears a certain resemblance to the ordinary photospheric granulation, although the spatial and temporal scales are, of course, much larger. The velocity field is so well ordered and long lived that it is highly suggestive of the flow patterns observed in cellular convection (cf. Section 4.4.2). Leighton *et al.* therefore came to the conclusion that the horizontal velocity field was to be identified with a giant system of convection currents, which they named the 'supergranulation', a term that has since found general acceptance.

Most of the main quantitative parameters pertaining to the supergranulation now seem fairly well established. The available data may be briefly summarized as follows:

(1) *Mean cell size.* Leighton, Noyes, and Simon [1962] found that at any given time there are roughly 2500 cells on the visible solar hemisphere. From

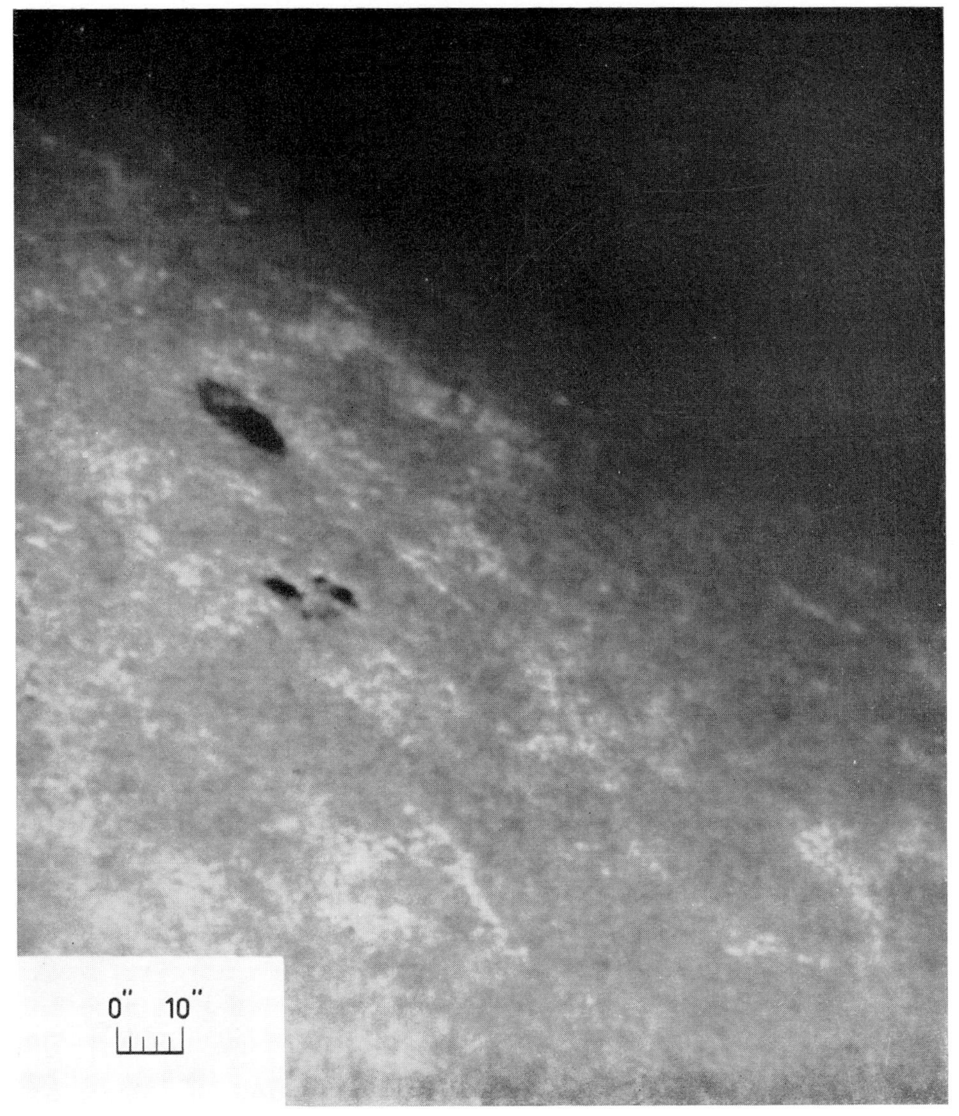

PLATE 3.1. Extended facular region surrounding a small sunspot group near the east limb (June 7, 1960). Each facular area is composed of a loose conglomeration of individual bright facular granules 1–2″ of arc in diameter, superimposed on a background of normal photospheric brightness. Note that in most cases the facular granules are not sufficiently compacted to form a pattern; some occur as completely isolated structures.

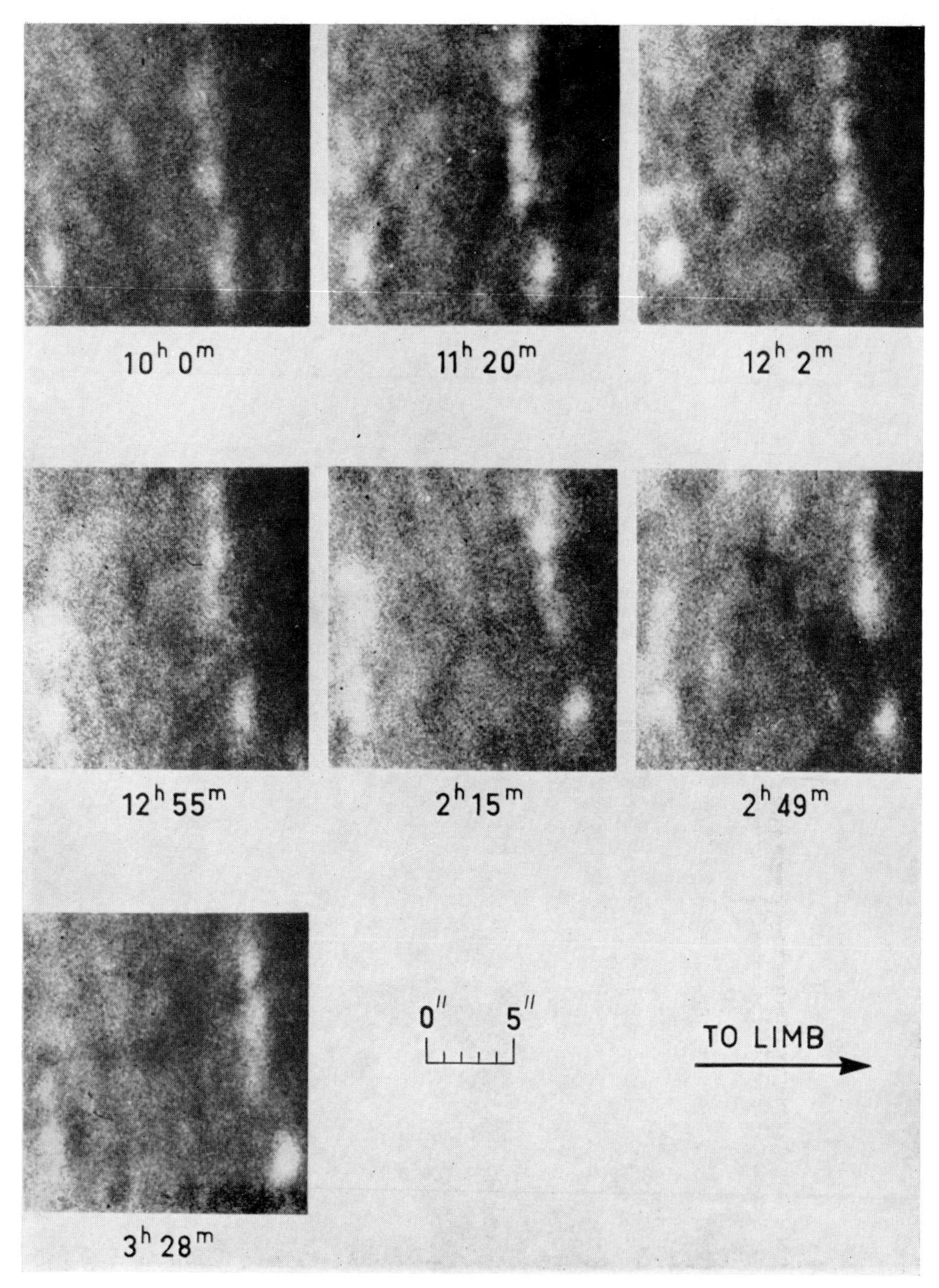

PLATE 3.2. Sequence illustrating the stability of individual facular granules in a small region near the east limb over a period of $5\frac{1}{2}$ hours. There are some changes due to the growth of new granules, but two granules situated in the lower corners of the photographs persist throughout the sequence. The apparent increase in the separation of these granules is due to solar rotation, the heliocentric angle of the centre of the region changing from 78° at $10^h\ 0^m$ to 75° at $3^h\ 28^m$.

PLATE 3.3. Doppler photograph of the Sun showing the large-scale distribution of horizontal motions constituting the supergranulation [Leighton, 1963]. Light and dark areas indicate velocities directed towards and away from the observer, respectively (the effect of solar rotation has been largely removed). The velocity field is made up of numerous velocity 'cells', each many thousands of kilometres in diameter, standing out against a grey (stationary) background. Note that in each case the line-of-sight velocity is directed towards the observer on the side of the cell facing towards the centre of the disk and away from the observer on the side facing the limb.

this one can immediately derive an estimate of the mean cell size, or the average distance between the centres of adjacent cells in the velocity pattern (cf. Section 2.2.3). If we call this distance d, the total number of cells must be of the order of $2\pi R^2/d^2$ (where R is the solar radius) and, equating this to the observed figure of 2500, we obtain

$$d \simeq 35{,}000 \text{ km}$$

for the mean cell size of the supergranulation pattern. Like the photospheric and umbral granulations, the supergranulation exhibits a fairly large spread in the individual cell sizes which, according to the results of an autocorrelation analysis carried out by Simon and Leighton [1964: cf. Fig. 4], range from 20,000 to 54,000 km.

(2) *Lifetime.* The observations of Hart [1956] and of Leighton, Noyes, and Simon [1962] show that the individual velocity cells have lifetimes of at least several hours. More precise measurements are difficult to make since the cells, being virtually invisible in the central region of the disk, have to be studied at heliocentric angles where the geometrical foreshortening is rather severe. However, Simon and Leighton [1964] have shown that a strong spatial correspondence exists between the cell boundaries and the network of bright calcium K-line faculae in the overlying chromosphere and, on this basis, they suggest that the lifetimes of the velocity cells are probably comparable to those of the elements of the K-network. They find that the latter last for periods of the order of 20 hr, in essential agreement with the results obtained independently by Macris [1962].

(3) *Magnitude of the horizontal velocities.* The measurements of a number of different observers [Hart, 1956; Evans and Michard, 1962; Simon and Leighton, 1964] agree in giving values of the order of 0·3–0·5 km/sec for the average peak horizontal velocities within the individual cells.

(4) *Existence of vertical velocities.* If the interpretation of the horizontal velocity field in terms of a system of convection cells is correct, then one should expect to find evidence of vertical velocities at both the centres and boundaries of the individual cells. And, indeed, on a few of their best Doppler photographs Simon and Leighton [1964] have detected in the central region of the disk a *very faint* pattern of rising velocities at the centre of each cell and a network of descending motions at the cell boundaries. As Simon [1964] has shown, the difficulty in observing the vertical components of the large-scale convection system is due to the presence of the prominent (and apparently quite unrelated) small-scale regime of vertical oscillatory velocities associated with the photospheric granulation, which we have described in Section 2.4.2. Nevertheless, by applying an appropriate method of time-smoothing to a series of spectrograms taken at the Sacramento Peak Observatory, Simon has been able to obtain independent confirmation of the existence of downward velocities of the order of 0·1–0·2 km/sec at the boundaries of the supergranules.

TABLE 3.1

Summary of Properties of Photospheric Granules and Other Analogous Photospheric Structures

FEATURE	DIAMETER	MEAN CELL SIZE (average separation)	LIFETIME	VELOCITY	LIMIT OF VISIBILITY (dist. from limb)	SECTION*
Photospheric granules	1–2″	2″.5	~10 min	vertical; 0·2 km/sec	≤5″	2.2–2.4
Umbral granules	0·4–2″ (range)	<2″.0	15–30 min	?	<25″	3.2; **3.6**
Penumbral filaments	0″.4	~1″.0	~2 hr	horizontal (Evershed velocity); 1–2 km/sec	?	**3.5.4**
Penumbral bright regions: Type 1	1–3″ (range)	—	30 min	?	?	**3.5.6**
Facular granules	1–2″	—	2 hr	?	1–2″	3·3
Supergranulation	30–70″ (range)	48″	>several hours	mainly horizontal; 0·3–0·5 km/sec	—	3·4

* Section numbers in **bold type** refer to the authors' [1964] monograph, those in ordinary type to the present work.
(*Note:* 1″ = 725 km)

The supergranulation is a relatively newly-observed phenomenon, but it is already clear that it is of fundamental importance. Not only does it form part of the basic hierarchy of organized motions in the photosphere but, in addition, according to Simon and Leighton [1964], it is closely related both to the large-scale distribution of weak magnetic fields in the photosphere and to various phenomena in the overlying chromosphere, such as the network of K-faculae. The large cell size of the supergranulation compared with that of the photospheric granulation suggests that it owes its origin to convective instability occurring at much greater depths. Further remarks on the interpretation of the supergranulation are reserved for the chapter that follows (Section 4.5.3).

3.5 Summary of Data

To conclude this brief review of the relationship between the photospheric granulation and other analogous photospheric structures, we summarize in Table 3.1 the known quantitative data concerning the main physical properties of the various structures discussed as well as, for comparison, the corresponding data for the photospheric granules. Also included are the data for penumbral filaments and penumbral bright regions. This table provides a useful bird's-eye view of the similarities and dissimilarities among the various photospheric features, but for more comprehensive information the reader should refer to the appropriate sections of this or the authors' previous book [Bray and Loughhead, 1964]. For convenience, the relevant section numbers are given in the last column of the table.

REFERENCES

BRAY, R. J., and LOUGHHEAD, R. E. [1961] 'Facular granule lifetimes determined with a seeing-monitored photoheliograph', *Aust. J. Phys.* **14**, 14.

BRAY, R. J., and LOUGHHEAD, R. E. [1964] *Sunspots.* (Chapman and Hall: London).

BRUGGENCATE, P. TEN [1940] 'Über die Natur der Fackeln auf der Sonnenscheibe. I. Fackelgranulen und ihre mittlere Lebensdauer', *Z. Astrophys.* **19**, 59.

BRUGGENCATE, P. TEN [1942] 'Über die Natur der Fackeln auf der Sonnenscheibe. II. Photometrie von Fackelgebieten', *Z. Astrophys.* **21**, 162.

BUMBA, V. [1965] 'Some notes on sunspot fine structure'. (*Stellar and Solar Magnetic Fields*, ed. R. LÜST, p. 305; North-Holland Publ. Co.: Amsterdam).

DANIELSON, R. E. [1964a] 'The structure of sunspot umbras. I. Observations', *Astrophys. J.* **139**, 45.

DANIELSON, R. E. [1964b] 'Observations of sunspot fine structure from the stratosphere and theoretical interpretation'. (*Atti del Convegno sulle Macchie Solari, Florence, 1964*, p. 77; Rome: 1964).

EVANS, J. W., and MICHARD, R. [1962] 'Observational study of macroscopic inhomogeneities in the solar atmosphere. III. Vertical oscillatory motions in the solar photosphere', *Astrophys. J.* **136,** 493.

HART, A. B. [1954] 'Motions in the Sun at the photospheric level. IV. The equatorial rotation and possible velocity fields in the photosphere', *Mon. Not. R.A.S.* **114,** 17.

HART, A. B. [1956] 'Motions in the Sun at the photospheric level. VI. Large scale motions in the equatorial region', *Mon. Not. R.A.S.* **116,** 38.

LEIGHTON, R. B. [1963] 'The solar granulation', *Ann. Rev. Astron. Astrophys.* **1,** 19.

LEIGHTON, R. B., NOYES, R. W., and SIMON, G. W. [1962] 'Velocity fields in the solar atmosphere. I. Preliminary report', *Astrophys. J.* **135,** 474.

LÉVY, M. [1965] 'Observations de la "supergranulation" au spectrohéliographe double de Meudon', *C.R. Acad. Sci.* **260,** 806.

MACRIS, C. J. [1962] 'Studies on the flocculi of the solar chromosphere. Part 1. Life time of the flocculi', *Mem. Soc. Astron. Ital.* **33,** 3.

PLASKETT, H. H. [1936] 'Solar granulation', *Mon. Not. R.A.S.* **96,** 402.

ROGERSON, J. B. [1961] 'On photospheric faculae', *Astrophys. J.* **134,** 331.

RÖSCH, J. [1964] 'L'observation des structures fines des taches solaires à partir du sol'. (*Atti del Convegno sulle Macchie Solari, Florence, 1964*, p. 43; Rome: 1964).

SIMON, G. W. [1964] 'Calcium network and vertical velocities', *Trans. I.A.U.* **12B,** 164.

SIMON, G. W., and LEIGHTON, R. B. [1964] 'Velocity fields in the solar atmosphere. III. Large-scale motions, the chromospheric network, and magnetic fields', *Astrophys. J.* **140,** 1120.

WALDMEIER, M. [1940] 'Die Feinstruktur der Sonnenoberfläche', *Helv. Phys. Act.* **13,** 13.

WALDMEIER, M. [1955] *Ergebnisse und Probleme der Sonnenforschung*, 2nd ed. (Geest u. Portig: Leipzig).

CHAPTER 4

Convective Theories of the Origin of the Granulation

4.1 Introduction

As we have seen in Chapter 2, the photospheric granulation displays a clearly-defined *cellular* pattern with a relatively narrow distribution of cell sizes, the mean distance between the centres of adjacent granules being about 1800 km (Sections 2.1 and 2.2.3). This basic observational fact provides the chief reason for regarding the granulation as a convective phenomenon: the only physical mechanism known to produce such a pattern in a fluid is buoyancy-driven convection, apart from surface tension and other agencies known to be absent. This conclusion is supported by the existence of a strong correlation in sense, although not in magnitude, between brightness and velocity in the photosphere, about 70 per cent of the bright features showing violet Doppler shifts (upward-moving material) and 70 per cent of the dark features showing red shifts (Sections 2.4.1 and 2.4.3).

Moreover, convective instability is a necessary consequence of the presence of a zone of partial ionization of the dominant element, hydrogen, a few hundred kilometres below the solar surface. An elementary volume of gas moving upwards through such a region of rapidly-decreasing ionization liberates ionization energy which, in turn, is converted to thermal energy. Thus the buoyancy of the elementary volume is increased and it continues its upward journey, provided the forces opposing its motion are sufficiently small.

Our chief aim in this chapter is to provide a proper theoretical basis for interpreting the observed properties of the photospheric granulation and supergranulation, in so far as the current state of the theory of convection permits. In pursuing this aim, we have not hesitated to include not only discussions of astrophysical convection in general and the solar hydrogen convection zone in particular, but also an account of modern work on the theory of convection by a number of theoretical hydrodynamicists. It seems to us that much of the latter work, especially a number of valuable papers by various authors in the *Journal of Fluid Mechanics*, is not sufficiently well known to solar physicists although it throws useful light on some of the problems of solar convection.

The subject matter of this chapter is inherently difficult and complex, but we have tried to develop the account in such a way as to make the subject accessible both to solar physicists and astrophysicists with no expert knowledge of modern fluid mechanics and to theoretical hydrodynamicists with no previous experience of solar physics.

We begin (Section 4.2.1) by considering the marginal instability of a horizontal layer of incompressible fluid heated from below – the classical Rayleigh problem – and, in particular, the definition of the Rayleigh number R. The magnitude of R, a dimensionless parameter which depends on the temperature gradient in the fluid and on its physical properties, determines whether or not the fluid is convectively unstable. The condition for instability can be written $R > R_{crit}$, where R_{crit} is approximately equal to 1000, the exact value depending on the boundary conditions. However, R actually has a far wider significance because both observation and theory show that for fluids which are beyond the state of marginal instability, the character of the convection depends mainly on the magnitude of R/R_{crit}.

An attempt to evaluate the Rayleigh number for the solar convection zone is made in Section 4.2.2. When the calculation is carried out using the ordinary atomic viscosity of the solar gases, the resulting value is far too big for the relatively well-ordered convection pattern which we actually observe. However, when the calculation is repeated using the 'eddy viscosity', the value of R is much reduced. The eddy viscosity represents the dissipative effects of non-linear interactions between different convective modes in a fluid well beyond the state of marginal instability, but its exact calculation unfortunately lies beyond the development of existing theory.

A brief mention is then made of the 'mixing-length' theory (Section 4.2.3) introduced by the German aerodynamicist L. Prandtl in the early 1930's which, although it has been extensively applied to solar and stellar convection zones, ignores virtually all details of the hydrodynamic processes occurring. Next we consider modern applications of the linearized theory of convection (Sections 4.3.1 and 4.3.2). Linearized theory is a simplified hydrodynamic treatment applicable only in the case of marginal instability; this implies that the Rayleigh number R only slightly exceeds R_{crit} or, alternatively, that the disturbances in density, pressure, temperature, etc., are of infinitesimal amplitude.

Of particular interest in these discussions is the method of taking into account a feature of astrophysical convection not normally encountered in laboratory convection, namely, the large density variation between the top and bottom of the convection zone. Two methods of approach are described. The first is the method of *polytropic atmospheres* (Section 4.3.1), which has been adopted by numerous authors. In this method the density variation is assumed to follow a law of the form $\rho = bz^m$, where z is the depth and m is the polytropic index. A second and more satisfactory approach (Section 4.3.2) is to apply the linearized hydrodynamic equations to a 'real' atmosphere, namely, a zero-order approximation to the actual solar convection zone derived from mixing-length theory. In this way K. H. Böhm has been able to compute, amongst other things, the magnitudes of the convective velocity components as functions of z (Figs. 4.3–4.6).

A basic aim of the various treatments based on linearized theory has been to predict the dominant scale of the photospheric granulation pattern, the magnitude of which is now well established by observation (cf. Section 2.2.3). In this, however, linearized theory has been unsuccessful: instead, it predicts a wide distribution of sizes extending to values well below the peak of the observed distribution curve (Fig. 4.2). In fact, one has to conclude that linearized theory falls far short of an adequate description of the phenomenon of the solar granulation. Some of its more fundamental limitations are listed in Section 4.3.3.

In non-linear theory, one considers finite perturbations in the various physical quantities and R/R_{crit} can take any value greater than unity. However, owing to mathematical difficulties, the development of this theory is still in its infancy and very few attempts have yet been made to apply it to the interpretation of the solar granulation. Hence in Section 4.4.2 we confine ourselves to outlining a few highlights of modern non-linear treatments which illustrate some of the progress achieved to date. After indicating the basic mathematical approach, the topics dealt with include the effect of gradually increasing R/R_{crit} on the mean temperature gradient (Fig. 4.7); the pattern of isotherms in a convection cell (Fig. 4.8); the preferred shape of the cells; and the direction of circulation and the morphology of the streamlines in a cell (Figs. 4.9 and 4.10). This list of topics gives some idea of the detailed results which non-linear theory is potentially capable of yielding.

Laboratory experiments having much relevance to solar convection are unfortunately few and far between, largely because most such experiments have been carried out with liquids rather than gases. However, the results of experiments having a bearing on the modern theoretical developments are briefly described in Section 4.4.3, with particular reference to results obtained at large values of R/R_{crit}.

The question of the theoretical interpretation of some of the observed properties of the granulation and supergranulation is discussed in Sections 4.5.2 and 4.5.3 respectively. Bearing in mind the inadequacies of existing theory, this discussion is necessarily incomplete; our aim is rather to confront existing theoretical ideas with just a few of the basic observational facts. For the granulation the topics discussed include the mean cell size, the lifetime, visibility near the extreme limb, the oscillatory velocity field, and the direction of circulation in a cell; for the supergranulation the discussion is restricted to the cell size. Two intriguing features of the supergranulation are emphasized, namely (a) its observation as a *velocity* but not as an *intensity* pattern, and (b) its apparent lack of any distorting effect on the ordinary granulation pattern. The possibility of cellular motions having a scale larger even than that of the supergranulation is mentioned.

Finally, in Section 4.6 we leave the realm of hydrodynamics and consider another theoretical aspect of the granulation, namely, the important question of the derivation of inhomogeneous photospheric models. An inhomogeneous

TABLE 4.1

*Principal Symbols Used in Chapter 4**

Symbol	Meaning
c_p	specific heat at constant pressure
E	internal energy per unit volume
$\mathbf{F}$	thermal flux vector
$\mathbf{g}$	acceleration due to gravity ($2{\cdot}74\times 10^4$ cm sec^{-2} at solar surface)
h	thickness of convecting layer
I	ionization energy per unit volume
k	Boltzmann constant ($1{\cdot}380\times 10^{-16}$ erg deg^{-1})
$\bar{k}$	Rosseland mean mass absorption coefficient
K	horizontal wave-number
m	polytropic index
m_{H}	mass of hydrogen atom ($1{\cdot}673\times 10^{-24}$ gm)
n	convective growth rate
p	fluid pressure
R	Rayleigh number
R_{crit}	critical Rayleigh number
T	temperature
$\mathbf{v}$	fluid velocity vector
w	vertical component of velocity
α	coefficient of thermal expansion
β	temperature gradient
γ	ratio of specific heats of gas
η	coefficient of viscosity
κ	coefficient of thermal diffusion; attenuation coefficient (Section 4.6.3)
κ_r	coefficient of thermal (radiative) conductivity
λ	horizontal wavelength of a convective mode
μ	mean molecular weight of gas
ν	coefficient of kinematic viscosity
ν_e	coefficient of eddy viscosity
ρ	fluid density
σ	Stefan constant ($5{\cdot}669\times 10^{-5}$ erg cm^{-2} deg^{-4} sec^{-1})
σ^*	Prandtl number ($=\nu/\kappa$)
τ	optical depth in continuum

* C.g.s. units are used throughout.

model is one that gives expression to horizontal as well as vertical variations in such physical quantities as the temperature, pressure, density, absorption coefficient, etc. Attempts to derive models based on observations of Fraunhofer lines are described in Section 4.6.2, while attempts based on the application of the new technique of non-uniform radiative transfer theory to observations made in integrated radiation are described in Section 4.6.3. Owing to a lack of adequate observational data, even the most recent inhomogeneous models must be regarded as extremely tentative and any detailed numerical results should be viewed with great caution. On the other hand, the derivation of an adequate inhomogeneous model of the convection zone will be required before exact expression can be given to the form of the radiative term or terms which occur in the basic hydrodynamic equations governing astrophysical convection.

4.2 The Classical Rayleigh Problem and Early Theoretical Work on Solar Convection

4.2.1 THE CLASSICAL RAYLEIGH PROBLEM

Let us suppose that we have a fluid, either gaseous or liquid, confined between two horizontal plates separated by a distance h and maintained

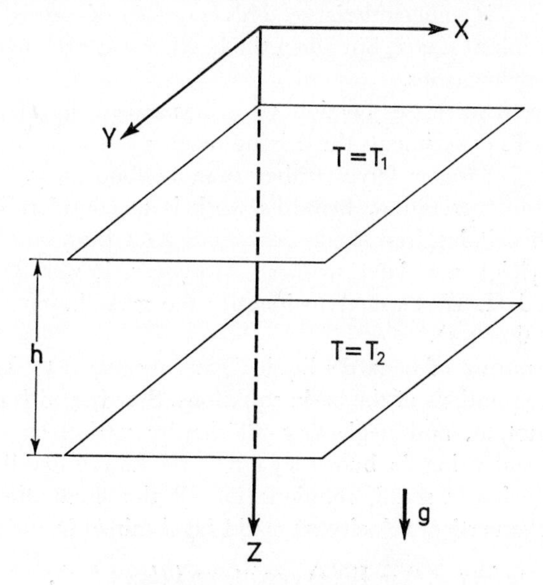

Fig. 4.1. Co-ordinate system

at temperatures T_1 (upper) and T_2 (lower), with $T_2 > T_1$ (see Fig. 4.1). Let us further suppose that the fluid has a positive coefficient of thermal expansion α, which will certainly be the case for a gas and for a normal liquid. Under these conditions it is clear that fluid near the lower plate will tend to rise. This tendency, however, will be opposed by two effects: (*a*) viscous dissipation, and (*b*) thermal diffusion in the fluid. One might speculate, therefore, that convection will occur only when the imposed temperature gradient $\beta = (T_2 - T_1)/h$ is sufficiently large or, alternatively, for a given β, when the coefficients of kinematic viscosity ν and of thermal diffusion κ are sufficiently small. And, in fact, one would expect the condition for the onset of convective instability to involve these three quantities (β, ν, and κ) as well as the coefficient of thermal expansion of the fluid α and the acceleration due to gravity g, the latter two parameters (together with β) establishing the magnitude of the buoyancy force which drives the convection currents.

Lord Rayleigh [1916] was the first to attempt a theoretical analysis of the problem of the onset of convection under these conditions. Rayleigh's investigation was inspired by the laboratory experiments of H. Bénard, which were carried out at the beginning of the present century.[1] Bénard worked with thin liquid layers, about 1 mm deep, standing on a heated metal plate kept at a uniform temperature. The upper surface was usually a free boundary in contact with the air. Bénard employed a number of liquids in his experiments; some of these are solids at ordinary temperatures. The outstanding result of Bénard's experiments was that the fluid layer resolves itself into a *cellular* pattern if β is sufficiently large. This consisted of somewhat irregular polygons in the initial stages, but when the heating was prolonged became a system of regular hexagons.

However, recent work (see Section 4.4.3) has shown that under the conditions of Bénard's experiments the driving mechanism was almost certainly provided by *surface tension* forces rather than by buoyancy. Nevertheless, despite this misinterpretation, Bénard's work is of considerable historical importance, since it inspired theoretical studies on buoyancy-driven convection by Rayleigh and later workers. Moreover, it was Bénard's work that in 1936 led H. H. Plaskett to identify the granulation with cellular convection (Section 1.4).

The cellular nature of Bénard's liquid layers suggested to Rayleigh that he seek periodic solutions of the basic equations. Starting with the Eulerian equations of motion, and neglecting all density variations except those responsible for generating the buoyancy forces, he showed that if the disturbances were sufficiently small, solutions for all the fluctuating quantities involved (e.g. the vertical velocity w) could be obtained in the form

$$w(x, y, z, t) = W(z) \exp nt \exp i(k_x x + k_y y). \qquad (4.1)$$

Subsequent authors have called n the *growth rate*, while the quantity $K = \sqrt{(k_x^2 + k_y^2)}$ is termed the *horizontal wave-number*. Sometimes, instead of K, the *horizontal wavelength* $\lambda = 2\pi/K$ is employed. The growth rate n is a function of K, and many of the modern discussions of linearized solutions of the form (4.1) in various physical situations, including the solar convection zone, centre on the variation of n with K and, in particular, on the value of K for which n is a maximum. It is implicitly assumed that this represents the wave-number of the dominant mode, i.e. the scale of the brightness or velocity variations actually observed (see Section 4.3.1). Finally, it should

[1] For references to Bénard's papers, see Rayleigh [1916] and Scriven and Sternling [1964].

be noted that $W(z)$ may itself be periodic in z: if $W(z) = 0$ only at the boundaries of the convecting layer, then the solution represented by (4.1) is called a *fundamental mode*. On the other hand, if $W(z)$ has one or more zeros within the layer, the corresponding solutions are called *harmonic modes* (cf. Section 4.5.3).

The condition for convective instability derived by Rayleigh may be expressed by the inequality

$$R > R_{\text{crit}}. \tag{4.2}$$

The quantity R is termed the *Rayleigh number* and, in the notation defined above, is given by the expression

$$R = \frac{g\alpha\beta h^4}{\kappa\nu}. \tag{4.3}$$

It is easy to see from (4.3) that R is *dimensionless*, since the units for both the coefficients of thermal diffusion κ and kinematic viscosity ν are $(\text{length})^2/\text{time}$. (This is in fact the reason for using κ and ν rather than the coefficient of thermal conductivity, which equals $\rho c_p \kappa$, and the ordinary coefficient of viscosity, $\eta = \rho\nu$.)

R_{crit} is the limiting value which R must exceed for convection to occur; it depends on the boundary conditions of the particular physical problem under consideration. For the problem studied by Rayleigh (both boundaries rigid, but permitting slip),

$$R_{\text{crit}} = \frac{27\pi^4}{4} = 657{\cdot}5. \tag{4.4}$$

In a subsequent analysis, Pellew and Southwell [1940] paid particular attention to the question of a more realistic choice of boundary conditions and also to the effect on R_{crit} of alternative boundary conditions. They found that for two free surfaces, R_{crit} has the same value as that given by (4.4), but for two rigid boundaries *not* permitting slip, R_{crit} is increased to 1708. For one free surface and one rigid boundary, not permitting slip, R_{crit} takes the value 1101.

Besides obtaining the criterion (4.2) for convective instability, Rayleigh [1916] also derived the horizontal wavelength of the first mode to become unstable. This quantity, which can be compared with observation, depends on the layer depth and the boundary conditions. The success of Rayleigh's hydrodynamic treatment acted as a stimulus to a number of other theoretical physicists who, while applying essentially the same linearized equations that Rayleigh had employed, explored the mathematics of the problem in greater detail.

In addition to Pellew and Southwell, other theoreticians who have made substantial contributions include H. Jeffreys, A. R. Low, and S. Chandrasekhar. To select just one point of interest, the latter author has investigated in considerable mathematical detail the effects of rotation and of a magnetic field on the onset of convection. He finds, for example, that a Coriolis force inhibits the onset of instability to an extent which depends on the value of a non-dimensional parameter (called the Taylor number)

$$C = \frac{4h^4\Omega^2}{\nu^2}, \tag{4.5}$$

where h is the layer depth and Ω is the vertical component of the angular velocity vector [Chandrasekhar, 1953; Chandrasekhar and Elbert, 1955].[2] Chandrasekhar's [1961] monograph *Hydrodynamic and Hydromagnetic Stability* provides a detailed account of theoretical work on the onset of convection in the presence of rotation and a magnetic field. Experimental work carried out under his direction at the University of Chicago has been summarized by Nakagawa and Prendergast [1958].

4.2.2 THE RAYLEIGH NUMBER FOR THE SOLAR CONVECTION ZONE

Turning now to the solar convection zone, it is apparent that the conditions there are very different from those obtaining in a convecting liquid. In the first place, the medium is a gas, whose compressibility cannot be ignored. Secondly, the thermal diffusivity is dominated by heat transfer due to radiation rather than molecular diffusion. Finally, we have to take account of the large density variation within the convection zone. The effect of these considerations is that, in the case of the Sun, we must give careful thought to the definition and evaluation of the various parameters appearing in the Rayleigh number (equation (4.3)).

(1) *The thermal diffusivity* κ. It can be shown that the contribution to the thermal flux vector **F** due to radiation far exceeds that due to thermal conduction [cf. Stepanov, 1949; Edmonds, 1957], so that following Ledoux and Walraven [1958: p. 444] and Böhm and Richter [1959], we may write

$$\mathbf{F} = -\kappa_r \operatorname{grad} T, \tag{4.6}$$

where

$$\kappa_r = \frac{16\sigma T^3}{3\bar{k}\rho} \tag{4.7}$$

is the coefficient of radiative conductivity. In (4.7) σ is Stefan's constant, $\bar{k}$ is the Rosseland mean mass absorption coefficient, and ρ is the density. However, as we have seen in Section 4.2.1, the quantity that must be substituted in (4.3) is the thermal diffusivity κ. Since $\kappa_r = \rho c_p \kappa$, we therefore have

$$\kappa = \frac{16\sigma T^3}{3\bar{k}c_p\rho^2}. \tag{4.8}$$

[2] Equation (4.5) has also been derived by Kuo [1954]; see also Khosla and Murgai [1963].

For a more complete discussion of the derivation of (4.8), the reader should consult Kuznetsova and Frank-Kamenetskii [1962]. Edmonds [1957] has tabulated κ_r as a function of temperature and gas pressure.

(2) *The kinematic viscosity* ν. Values of the atomic viscosity as a function of temperature and pressure have also been calculated by Edmonds [1957]. As a representative figure,

$$\nu = 2 \times 10^3 \text{ cm}^2/\text{sec} \tag{4.9}$$

at a point in the solar convection zone where $T = 8200°\text{K}$.

(3) *Coefficient of expansion* α. This may easily be evaluated from the formula

$$\alpha = -\frac{1}{\rho}\left(\frac{\partial \rho}{\partial T}\right)_p = \frac{1}{T} \tag{4.10}$$

for a perfect gas [Gille and Goody, 1964; Weiss, 1964].

(4) *The temperature gradient* β. In the case of a gas we have to replace the temperature gradient $\mathrm{d}T/\mathrm{d}z$ by the difference between the actual gradient and the adiabatic gradient, i.e.

$$\beta = \frac{\mathrm{d}T}{\mathrm{d}z} - \left(\frac{\mathrm{d}T}{\mathrm{d}z}\right)_{\text{ad}} \equiv \Delta \text{ grad } T, \text{ for short.} \tag{4.11}$$

The derivation of (4.11) hinges on a calculation of the buoyancy force experienced by a hot rising element which does not exchange heat with its surroundings [see Unsöld, 1955: p. 217].

In passing, we may remark that if the actual gradient equals or is less than the adiabatic gradient, the buoyancy force vanishes and convection cannot occur, regardless of the magnitudes of κ and ν. In fact, since β is then less than or equal to zero, we see from (4.3) that $R \leqslant 0$, and hence the condition for convective instability, $R > R_{\text{crit}}$, cannot be satisfied. The condition

$$\frac{\mathrm{d}T}{\mathrm{d}z} > \left(\frac{\mathrm{d}T}{\mathrm{d}z}\right)_{\text{ad}} \tag{4.12}$$

is known as the Schwarzschild criterion [K. Schwarzschild, 1906] and has been much used in calculating solar and stellar model convection zones. It is important to realize, however, that (4.12) is only a necessary, *but not a sufficient*, condition for convective instability. There is a range of temperature gradients which satisfy (4.12) but do not satisfy (4.2); throughout this range the gas is convectively stable.

In the solar convection zone β varies markedly with depth, being some 100 times larger in the very unstable layer assumed to be responsible for the photospheric granulation than in the deeper, less unstable layers [Böhm, 1958].

(5) *The effective layer thickness h*. In the case of the solar convection zone it is not easy to assign a precise value to this parameter since, although the whole zone (extending from $z = 505$ to $z = 63{,}000$ km – see Section 4.3.2)

is convectively unstable, the degree of instability varies markedly with depth. The most unstable layers are located near the top of the zone, a few hundred kilometres below the visible photosphere, and it is these that are believed to be responsible for the photospheric granulation (cf. Section 4.5.1). It seems reasonable to take the bottom of this highly unstable zone to be the level at which the hydrogen ionization energy begins to undergo a marked decrease with decreasing z. This occurs in the region $z = 800$–900 km (Section 4.5.2). The upper boundary is located at $\tau \simeq 1$, i.e. $z \simeq 500$ km; at this level the convecting elements begin to radiate away to outer space a substantial fraction of their thermal energy. Hence we obtain an estimate of

$$h = 350 \text{ km}$$

for the effective layer thickness.

Other authors have selected the local density or pressure scale heights, given by the formulae

$$h_\rho = \frac{dz}{d \ln \rho} \text{ and } h_p = \frac{dz}{d \ln p} \text{ respectively.}$$

On this basis Schwarzschild [1959] and Ledoux, Schwarzschild, and Spiegel [1961] assign h a value of 300 km.

Collecting together the new definitions of the various parameters comprised in the Rayleigh number, we can now re-write (4.3) in the form

$$R = \frac{gh^4}{\kappa \nu} \cdot \frac{\Delta \operatorname{grad} T}{T} \cdot \qquad (4.13)$$

In spite of the difficulties and uncertainties described above, Schwarzschild [1959] and Ledoux *et al.* [1961] have made actual estimates of the value of the Rayleigh number R for the solar convection zone. Taking h to be the density scale height, Schwarzschild calculates R for the layer at which $T = 8200$°K, assuming the following values for the various parameters: $T = 8200$°K, $\rho = 3 \times 10^{-7}$ gm/cm^3, $\log p = 5{\cdot}2$, $h = 300$ km, and $[(\gamma - 1)/T] \Delta \operatorname{grad} T = 1/4000 \text{ km}^{-1}$ [after Vitense, 1953]; and $\kappa = 2 \times 10^{12}$ cm^2/sec, $\nu = 2 \times 10^3$ cm^2/sec [after Edmonds, 1957].[3] The resulting value of R is

$$R_1 = 1{\cdot}4 \times 10^{10},$$

which is some seven orders of magnitude larger than the values of R_{crit} ($\simeq 10^3$) derived by Pellew and Southwell (cf. Section 4.2.1). This figure appears to be far too big for the relatively well-ordered granulation pattern which we actually observe. In fact, experiments on laboratory fluids indicate that convective flow patterns become completely disordered when R attains values of the order of 10^6, or even somewhat less (Section 4.4.3).

[3] Schwarzschild's formula for R differs from that given in (4.13) by the factor $\gamma - 1$.

A similar calculation by Ledoux *et al.*, employing slightly different values for some of the parameters, yields

$$R_1 = 2 \times 10^{11}.$$

However, the above calculations of the Rayleigh number have been made on the implicit assumption that the only form of energy dissipation is that due to atomic viscosity. On the other hand, in the case of well-developed convection – such as that in the solar convection zone – an additional source of damping can arise from the effects of *non-linear interactions* involving a hierarchy of convective modes having wavelengths small compared to that of the dominant, observed mode. It is possible, in a very crude sort of way, to take account of the effects of non-linear interactions on the calculation of R by introducing an effective coefficient of viscosity, usually referred to as the *eddy viscosity* ν_e.[4] Unfortunately, calculation of this quantity presents almost insuperable difficulties at the present time although, in principle, it could be calculated if we knew the full range of wavelengths present, together with their interactions. This is, in fact, one of the aims of non-linear convection theory, which we shall discuss in Section 4.4. However, at the present time the application of non-linear theory to the solar convection zone is still in its infancy.

Nevertheless, a calculation by Schwarzschild [1959] does at least demonstrate that the eddy viscosity is likely to be much larger than the atomic viscosity. This author applied the following rule of thumb, derived from laboratory experience:

$$\nu_e = \tfrac{1}{10} V\lambda,$$

where V is a characteristic velocity and λ is the linear scale of the convection pattern. Taking $V = 0{\cdot}2$ km/sec (Section 2.4) and $\lambda = 1800$ km (Section 2.2.3), this rule gives

$$\nu_e = 4 \times 10^{11}\ \text{cm}^2/\text{sec}. \tag{4.14}$$

This may be compared with the figure of 2×10^3 cm^2/sec quoted above for the atomic viscosity at a point in the convection zone where $T = 8200$°K.

Using the value given by (4.14) for the eddy viscosity, Schwarzschild repeated his calculation of the Rayleigh number for the solar convection zone and obtained the result

$$R_2 \simeq 100.$$

This value is now well *below* the critical value for the onset of convection.

Summarizing, we can draw two conclusions from the various calculations described above. In the first place, calculation of R on the basis of the atomic

[4] As the name implies, this is actually a concept borrowed from the theory of aerodynamic turbulence [see, for example, Batchelor, 1953: p. 113]. However, in the present context it represents the dissipative effects of non-linear interactions between different *convective* modes and must not be taken as implying the existence of a fine-scale turbulence (in the aerodynamic sense) in the solar granulation (cf. Section 1.5).

viscosity alone gives a value which seems to be far too big for the relatively well-ordered convection pattern which we actually observe; this implies that some of the dissipation (perhaps a major part) must be due to non-linear interactions. Secondly, the rule of thumb for the eddy viscosity quoted above evidently gives much too large a value in the case of the Sun. A correct calculation of this important parameter, and hence of the Rayleigh number itself, requires further development of non-linear convection theory.

To complete this discussion of the calculation of the Rayleigh number for the solar convection zone, it is of interest to enquire whether or not solar rotation has any significant stabilizing influence. The necessary calculations have been carried out by Chandrasekhar [1953] who, substituting $\Omega = 2{\cdot}9 \times 10^{-6}\,\text{sec}^{-1}$, $\nu = 5 \times 10^{3}\,\text{cm}^2/\text{sec}$ in equation (4.5) above, finds that for $h = 10^6$ cm $= 10$ km, i.e. for $C = 10^6$, the critical Rayleigh number is increased over its value for *no* rotation by a factor of 140. He therefore concludes that in the case of the Sun, rotation is a powerful stabilizing influence even for comparatively thin layers. This conclusion, however, depends on the choice of ν: if instead of the atomic viscosity we use the value of the eddy viscosity given by (4.14), namely $\nu_e = 4 \times 10^{11}$ cm^2/sec, then C is reduced to a negligible quantity and no increase in R_{crit} results. In any event, regardless of the value of ν, rotation has no effect at the solar equator, since the vertical component of the angular velocity vector is there zero.

4.2.3 OTHER THEORETICAL APPROACHES: THE MIXING-LENGTH THEORY

While the workers referred to in Section 4.2.1 were developing the classical hydrodynamic theory of convective instability, a radically simplified treatment, called the 'mixing-length' theory, was being applied to the convection zones of the Sun and stars by a number of theoretical astrophysicists; these included H. Siedentopf, R. Woolley, L. Biermann, C. de Jager, and particularly E. Böhm-Vitense [for references, see Aller, 1963: p. 454]. The concept of the mixing-length was first introduced by the famous German aerodynamicist L. Prandtl in the early 1930's. The fundamental basis of the theory is the assumption that the convective energy is carried by 'eddies' which part with their energy and momentum after travelling a certain distance H. This quantity, which is termed the mixing-length, is thus analogous to the molecular mean free path in the kinetic theory of gases. With the aid of this and other assumptions, it is possible to derive expressions for the convective energy transport, the gas velocity, and the temperature difference between the hot and cold elements. In more recent times, however, serious criticisms of the mixing-length theory have been voiced by numerous authors on the grounds that it incorporates several arbitrary or otherwise unsatisfactory features [see, for example, Pecker, 1959; Böhm, 1963a].[5]

[5] For detailed accounts of the mixing-length theory and its application to the calculation of model convection zones, the reader is referred to Vitense [1953], Unsöld [1955], and Spiegel [1963].

Nevertheless, the application of the mixing-length theory to the Sun does at least furnish a *zero-order approximation* to the solar convection zone upon which a more exact treatment can be based. For example, Böhm [1963a] has applied first-order (i.e. linearized) convection theory to Böhm-Vitense's [1958] mixing-length theory model of the zone; Böhm's work is described in detail in Section 4.3.2. It is important to realize, however, that the mixing-length theory calmly ignores virtually all details of the actual hydrodynamic processes that occur in a convecting fluid. Hence calculations of the structure of the solar convection zone based on this theory should be regarded as essentially phenomenological; actual numerical results should be viewed with great prudence except as a zero-order approximation [Pecker, 1959].

The period under review in the present section can be summarized by remarking that although much fundamental work was carried out, little of this could be successfully applied to the solar convection zone. On the one hand, the mixing-length theory, although capable of producing numerical results, was crude and unsatisfactory from the theoretical point of view. On the other hand, the more refined hydrodynamic treatments along the lines initiated by Rayleigh, while laying the foundations for future theoretical investigations, did not take into account the large density gradients that occur in astrophysical systems. In subsequent sections of this chapter we shall see how this limitation has now been removed.

Numerous review articles have been published on the theory of convection. These include brief reviews of early work contained in articles by Palm [1960], Nield [1964], and Scriven and Sternling [1964], while a convenient compilation by Saltzman [1962] collects in one volume a number of important papers by Rayleigh, Jeffreys, Low, Pellew and Southwell, Kuo, Chandrasekhar, and others. Finally, reviews of theoretical work on convection with particular emphasis on astrophysical applications are to be found in papers by Böhm and Richter [1959], Pecker [1959], and Unno, Kato, and Makita [1960]. Pecker's lengthy review paper is of particular value for its critical approach, for example to the mixing-length theory, and for its extensive bibliography: this extends from K. Schwarzschild's [1906] paper (see Section 4.2.2) to more modern investigations published up to 1958.

4.3 Modern Applications of Linearized Theory to the Solar Convection Zone

4.3.1 METHOD OF POLYTROPIC ATMOSPHERES

A basic limitation of most of the work described in the previous sections, as far as astrophysical applications are concerned, is the requirement that the density ρ remain constant with depth. In recent years, however, a number of workers, starting with Skumanich [1955], have sought to remove this limitation. The aim has been to develop a theory which has greater relevance to the actual conditions which obtain in the convection zones of the Sun and stars, where the density variation between the top and bottom of the entire zone may amount to several orders of magnitude (cf. Table 4.3).

One way of expressing the density variation is to assume a *polytropic model atmosphere*. By varying the polytropic index and other parameters, it is then possible to change the magnitude of the density variation and thus explore its influence on the convective solutions. It is true that a polytropic model can only be a highly schematic representation of a real atmosphere: for example, in a polytropic atmosphere the temperature increases only linearly with depth (equation (4.22) below), whereas in actual stellar atmospheres the increase is much steeper. Nevertheless, there has been a general expectation that the solutions of the convection equations for polytropic atmospheres would prove to have some relevance to convection in the Sun and stars and, in particular, to the interpretation of the photospheric granulation. For example, Spiegel [1964a] has sought to determine whether or not the curve expressing the growth rate n as a function of the horizontal wave-number K (cf. Section 4.2.1) possesses a maximum and, if so, whether or not this maximum can be identified with the dominant scale of the photospheric granulation pattern.

In order to give some idea of the polytropic approach, we shall briefly describe the work of Unno, Kato, and Makita [1960], whose particular aim was to determine how a density gradient influences the magnitude of the critical Rayleigh number. Unno *et al.* start with the following basic equations:

Conservation of momentum:

$$\rho \frac{\mathrm{d}\mathbf{v}}{\mathrm{d}t} = \rho \mathbf{g} - \operatorname{grad} p + \tfrac{1}{3}\eta \operatorname{grad}(\operatorname{div} \mathbf{v}) + \eta \nabla^2 \mathbf{v} \tag{4.15}$$

Conservation of mass:

$$\frac{\mathrm{d}\rho}{\mathrm{d}t} + \rho \operatorname{div} \mathbf{v} = 0 \tag{4.16}$$

Conservation of energy:

$$\rho c_p \frac{\mathrm{d}T}{\mathrm{d}t} - \frac{\mathrm{d}p}{\mathrm{d}t} = \operatorname{div}(\kappa_r \operatorname{grad} T) \tag{4.17}$$

Equation of state:

$$p = \frac{k\rho T}{\mu m_{\mathrm{H}}}. \tag{4.18}$$

In these equations the operator

$$\frac{\mathrm{d}}{\mathrm{d}t} = \frac{\partial}{\partial t} + \mathbf{v} \cdot \operatorname{grad}$$

indicates differentiation following the motion of the gas; $\eta = \rho\nu_e$ is the coefficient of viscosity (ν_e = kinematic (eddy) viscosity); and κ_r is the radiative conductivity. η, κ_r, and c_p are taken as constant throughout the analysis, and the ionization energy is taken to be zero.

The polytropic index is derived as follows: let the positive z-axis be parallel to the gravitational acceleration $\mathbf{g}$ (cf. Fig. 4.1). Then in the undisturbed static state, i.e. with $\mathbf{v} = 0$ and $\mathrm{d}/\mathrm{d}t = 0$, (4.15), (4.17), and (4.18) become

$$\frac{\mathrm{d}p_0}{\mathrm{d}z} = \rho_0 g \tag{4.19}$$

$$\frac{\mathrm{d}}{\mathrm{d}z}\left(\kappa_r \frac{\mathrm{d}T_0}{\mathrm{d}z}\right) = 0 \tag{4.20}$$

and

$$p_0 = \frac{k}{\mu m_{\mathrm{H}}} \cdot \rho_0 T_0, \tag{4.21}$$

the subscript '0' indicating undisturbed values. Upon integration, remembering that κ_r is constant, we have

$$\left.\begin{aligned} p_0 &= \frac{1}{1+m} g b z^{1+m} \\ \rho_0 &= b z^m \\ T_0 &= \beta_0 z \end{aligned}\right\} \tag{4.22}$$

where β_0, the temperature gradient, and b are constants of integration. The polytropic index m is not an independent constant but is related to β_0 by the equation

$$m = \frac{g}{(k/\mu m_{\mathrm{H}})\,\beta_0} - 1.$$

Unno *et al.* restrict their study to determining the condition for the onset of convection. The equation for marginal stability (their equation (24)) is derived by subtracting (4.19)–(4.21) from the corresponding equations (4.15)–(4.17) and is then solved subject to the following boundary conditions: (*a*) vertical velocity $w = 0$ at the top, $z = z_0$, and bottom, $z = z_0 + h$, of the convection zone; (*b*) temperature uniform over the horizontal boundary planes, $z = z_0$ and $z = z_0 + h$; and (*c*) no viscous shearing stresses parallel to the horizontal boundary surfaces, i.e.

$$\eta\left(\frac{\partial u}{\partial z} + \frac{\partial w}{\partial x}\right) = \eta\left(\frac{\partial v}{\partial z} + \frac{\partial w}{\partial y}\right) = 0$$

at $z = z_0$ and $z = z_0 + h$.

To facilitate the solution Unno *et al.* introduce the non-dimensional parameter

$$Z_0 = z_0/h$$

which, in effect, specifies the depth of the top of the convection zone in terms of its thickness. Using the second equation of (4.22), we readily see that the density ratio between the bottom and top of the zone is then

$$\frac{\rho_2}{\rho_1} = \left(\frac{Z_0 + 1}{Z_0}\right)^m.$$

Unno *et al.* then proceed to calculate the critical Rayleigh number R_{crit} for various values of Z_0 and m and thus for various values of the density variation. The results are shown in Table 4.2. It is clear that when the

TABLE 4.2

Critical Rayleigh Number as a Function of Density Variation
[*Unno et al., 1960*]

m	Z_0	ρ_2/ρ_1	R_{crit}
1	10	1.1	656
1	1·0	2	680
1	0·1	11	786
2	0·1	121	760

Note: values for R_{crit} are computed for a point midway between the top of the atmosphere and the bottom of the convection zone, not for the midpoint of the zone itself.

variation is small, R_{crit} is close to the value for free boundaries in the classical Rayleigh problem, namely 657·5 (cf. Section 4.2.1). For larger values of the density variation, however, R_{crit} begins to show a small but significant increase.

In order to determine what significance the results in Table 4.2 have for the solar convection zone, we need to know the appropriate values of ρ_2/ρ_1 for the photospheric granulation and the supergranulation. These are easily obtained from Table 4.3: taking the lower boundaries of the granulation and supergranulation layers to be located at z = 850 km and z = 7000 km respectively (Sections 4.5.2 and 4.5.3), and the upper boundary of both layers to be located at z = 500 km, we readily obtain ρ_2/ρ_1 = 1·9 for the granulation and ρ_2/ρ_1 = 195 for the supergranulation. The first figure lies well within the range considered by Unno *et al.*; the second lies somewhat outside this range, but probably by an insignificant amount. The analysis of

Unno *et al.* therefore leads us to the important conclusion that the critical Rayleigh numbers for the convecting layers responsible for both the granulation and the supergranulation are probably not significantly different from the value for free boundaries in the classical Rayleigh problem.

The problem of convection in a polytropic atmosphere has also been investigated by Böhm and Richter [1959]. These authors, however, neglected viscosity, thus ignoring the last two terms in (4.15). They carried out calculations for a polytropic index of $m = 1$, and their aims were twofold: (*a*) to determine the magnitudes of w, the vertical velocity, and of ΔT and $\Delta\rho$, the horizontal variations in temperature and density, as functions of the growth rate n; and (*b*) to establish whether or not the growth-rate curve showed a maximum at some particular wave-number. In a later paper, Böhm and Richter [1960] examined the effect on the solution of *superimposing a stable layer* upon the highly unstable polytrope, a situation which is very relevant to the solar case, as we shall see in the next section. They found that even with quite a thin layer, the rate of increase of instability with increasing wave-number is much slower than with no stable layer present. This interesting result is capable of a simple physical interpretation: the stable layer evidently tends to damp down the smaller disturbances, while allowing the larger ones to penetrate relatively unimpeded.[6]

In their second paper, Böhm and Richter allowed the polytropic index m in the unstable layer to vary from 0·11 to 1·22 and neglected radiative conductivity. In contradiction to their earlier calculations, they concluded that there was *no* well-defined wavelength of maximum instability, the growth rate showing a monotonic increase with wave-number.

Finally, a paper by Spiegel [1964a] pays particular attention to a more exact calculation of the radiative term in (4.17) for optically thin and optically thick disturbances, respectively; like Böhm and Richter, he neglects viscosity. Spiegel carries out his calculations for a polytropic index of $m = 6$, which corresponds to a less unstable polytrope than those employed by Unno *et al.* and by Böhm and Richter. His most important conclusion is that radiative exchanges do not change the qualitative dependence of the growth rate n on the horizontal wave-number K for most cases of astrophysical interest. In other words, n is generally a monotonic increasing function of K with no maximum that can, for example, be identified with the peak of the observed cell size distribution of the photospheric granulation. Any radiative cut-off must therefore occur at much smaller wavelengths than the smallest granules that we actually observe.

Spiegel's work, as does that of Böhm and Richter, accordingly reveals a profound disagreement between theory and observation. The application of the linearized theory to a polytropic atmosphere seems to yield solutions which are quite incapable of explaining one of the most prominent and basic features of the photospheric granulation, namely, the existence of a

[6] The phenomenon of penetration is further discussed in Section 4.5.2.

dominant cell size with a fairly steep cut-off on either side of the peak (Section 2.2.3 and Fig. 2.1).

4.3.2 BÖHM'S APPLICATION OF LINEARIZED THEORY TO A MODEL OF THE SOLAR CONVECTION ZONE

As we have seen in the previous section, the application of linearized convection theory to polytropic atmospheres yields solutions which disagree with the results of observation. Is this disagreement a consequence of the linearization of the hydrodynamic equations, i.e. the assumption that all quantities differ from their equilibrium values only by small amounts, the Rayleigh number being only slightly greater than R_{crit}? Or is it due to the fact that a polytropic atmosphere can only be a highly schematic representation of the real solar convection zone having, for example, a much less steep variation of temperature with depth than the actual variation?

In order to answer these questions, Böhm [1963a] has calculated some of the possible linear modes and their degrees of instability for a detailed model of the solar convection zone. Böhm's study is restricted to *fundamental* modes, i.e. those in which the amplitude of the vertical velocity ($W(z)$ in equation (4.1)) is zero only at the boundaries of the convecting layer. The model he takes as his starting point, which we may regard as a zero-order approximation to the actual convection zone, is substantially the same as Böhm-Vitense's [1958] mixing-length model (cf. Section 4.2.3). All the details implicit in this model are included in Böhm's calculations, namely: (*a*) the fairly complicated dependence of the mean temperature, density, internal energy, etc., on geometrical depth; (*b*) the depth dependence of the opacity $\bar{k}$ and the radiative conductivity κ_r; and (*c*) the existence of a stable photospheric layer on top of the unstable convection zone.

The model used by Böhm in his calculations is given in Table 4.3. For the stable part of the photosphere extending up to an optical depth of $\tau = 0{\cdot}03$, i.e. $z = 300$ km, the model is the same as the radiative equilibrium model of Böhm [1954a]. On top of this photospheric part there is a highly stable zone 300 km thick. This zone is assumed to be isothermal with a temperature of 4700°K and is identified with the photosphere–chromosphere boundary and the lower chromosphere. For the unstable part of the photosphere and the underlying region down to a geometrical depth of $z = 22{,}000$ km, the values are taken from Böhm-Vitense's model. Finally, from $z = 22{,}000$ km down to the bottom of the convection zone, $z = 63{,}000$ km, the model is approximated by a polytropic representation, ρ_0 and T_0 varying according to equations (4.22) above.

Böhm starts out with the following basic equations:

Conservation of momentum:

$$\rho \frac{d\mathbf{v}}{dt} = \rho \mathbf{g} - \operatorname{grad} p \qquad (4.23)$$

Conservation of mass:

$$\frac{\partial \rho}{\partial t} + \mathrm{div}\,(\rho \mathbf{v}) = 0 \tag{4.24}$$

Conservation of energy:

$$\rho\left[\frac{\mathrm{d}E_m}{\mathrm{d}t} + p\frac{\mathrm{d}\,(1/\rho)}{\mathrm{d}t}\right] = -\mathrm{div}\,\mathbf{F}, \tag{4.25}$$

where E_m is the internal energy per unit mass, $\mathbf{F}$ is the radiative flux given by

$$\mathbf{F} = -\frac{16\sigma}{3\bar{k}\rho} T^3 \,\mathrm{grad}\, T, \tag{4.6}$$

and all the other quantities have the meanings assigned to them in Table 4.1.

The internal energy is taken to be the sum of the thermal and ionization energies, the excitation energy being neglected. It is given by

$$\begin{aligned} E = \rho E_m &= \tfrac{3}{2} kT(N_0 + n_e) + N_0 \{\nu_H \chi_H x_H + \\ &\quad \nu_{He}\,[x_{HeI}\chi_{HeI} + x_{HeII}(\chi_{HeI} + \chi_{HeII})]\} \\ &= \tfrac{3}{2} p + I, \end{aligned} \tag{4.26}$$

where E = total energy, I = ionization energy, N_0 = total number of heavy particles, n_e = number of electrons – all per unit volume; ν_H and ν_{He} are the relative normalized hydrogen and helium abundances by number of atoms; x_H, x_{HeI}, and x_{HeII} are the appropriate degrees of ionization of hydrogen and helium; and χ_H, χ_{HeI}, and χ_{HeII} are the corresponding ionization potentials. Numerical values for E, I, and $(I/E) \times 100$ are given in the last three columns of Table 4.3.

Equations (4.23)–(4.25) differ from the corresponding basic equations (4.15)–(4.17) used by Unno, Kato, and Makita [1960] in two respects: (*a*) Unno *et al.* ignore the ionization energy I in their discussion, the convective instability in their treatment being brought about by an appropriate choice of the polytropic index, and therefore the temperature gradient, rather than by the liberation of ionization energy (when I is put equal to zero, the left-hand sides of (4.25) and (4.17) may be shown to be equal); and (*b*) Böhm neglects viscous forces, thus putting η in (4.15) equal to zero. Böhm's argument for this neglect rests on the high value of the Rayleigh number, which implies that the viscous forces are very small in comparison to the buoyancy forces. However, as we have seen in Section 4.2.2, when eddy viscosity is taken into account, the Rayleigh number is very substantially reduced, so that it is questionable whether Böhm's neglect of viscous forces is fully justified.

The linearization of (4.23)–(4.25) is carried out by substituting

$$\left.\begin{aligned} \rho &= \rho_0 + \rho^* \\ p &= p_0 + p^*, \text{ etc.,} \end{aligned}\right\} \tag{4.27}$$

TABLE 4.3

Zero-Order Model of the Solar Convection Zone [Böhm, 1963a]

z (km)	T_0 (°K)	ρ_0 (gm/cm³)	p_0 (dynes/cm²)	$\bar{k}_0$ (cm²/gm)	E_0 (ergs/cm³)	I_0 (ergs/cm³)	$(I_0/E_0) \times 100$ (per cent)
50	4.70×10^{3}	4.90×10^{-9}	1.31×10^{3}	1.02×10^{-2}	1.96×10^{3}	0	0
100	4.70	8.29	2.22	1.50	3.32	0	0
150	4.70	1.40×10^{-8}	3.75	2.17	5.63	0	0
200	4.70	2.38	6.37	3.44	9.55	0	0
250	4.70	4.02	1.07×10^{4}	5.37	1.61×10^{4}	0	0
300	4.72	6.83	1.83	7.91	2.75	0	0
350	4.88	1.11×10^{-7}	3.09	1.27×10^{-1}	4.63	0	0
400	5.20	1.67	4.95	1.99	7.42	0	0
450	5.66	2.66	8.57	3.19	1.29×10^{5}	0	0
500	6.13	2.99	1.04×10^{5}	7.06	1.57	0.01×10^{5}	0.6
550	8.19	3.20	1.50	8.56×10^{0}	2.45	0.20	8.2
600	1.02×10^{4}	3.68	2.24	5.01×10^{1}	5.03	1.67	33.2
650	1.10	4.04	2.74	1.01×10^{2}	7.20	3.09	42.9
700	1.16	4.35	3.20	1.56	9.47	4.67	49.4
750	1.21	4.69	3.76	2.10	1.24×10^{6}	0.68×10^{6}	54.8
800	1.26	5.09	4.34	2.60	1.54	0.89	57.8
850	1.29	5.56	5.01	3.00	1.86	1.11	59.7
900	1.34	6.08	5.83	3.56	2.29	1.42	62.0
950	1.38	6.65	6.73	4.26	2.75	1.74	63.3
1000	1.41	7.26	7.67	5.08	3.22	2.07	64.3
1100	1.48	8.85	1.01×10^{6}	7.05	4.41	2.89	65.6
1200	1.53	1.07×10^{-6}	1.30	9.35	5.77	3.82	66.3
1300	1.59	1.26	1.64	1.19×10^{3}	7.38	4.92	66.7
1400	1.64	1.48	2.03	1.45	9.25	6.20	67.1
1500	1.70	1.71	2.46	1.70	1.13×10^{7}	0.76×10^{7}	67.3
1600	1.75	1.98	2.99	1.94	1.37	0.92	67.2
1700	1.79	2.26	3.56	2.15	1.63	1.10	67.5
1800	1.84	2.57	4.19	2.33	1.92	1.29	67.2
1900	1.89	2.90	4.95	2.45	2.27	1.53	67.4
2000	1.94	3.26	5.76	2.50	2.63	1.77	67.3

2200	2·05	4·02	7·73	—	3·50	2·34	67·0
2400	2·15	4·89	$1·00 \times 10^{7}$	—	4·49	2·99	66·7
2600	2·27	5·89	1·30	—	5·74	3·79	66·1
2800	2·38	6·95	1·63	—	7·09	4·65	65·7
3000	2·48	8·13	2·02	—	8.66	5·63	65·0
3200	2·60	9·47	2·49	—	$1·06 \times 10^{8}$	$0·69 \times 10^{8}$	65·2
3400	2·71	$1·09 \times 10^{-5}$	3·02	—	1·26	0·81	64·3
3600	2·82	1·24	3·62	—	1·50	0·96	64·0
3800	2·94	1·40	4·31	—	1·76	1·11	63·2
4000	3·05	1·58	5·09	—	2·05	1·29	62·9
4200	3·18	1·77	6·00	—	2·39	1·49	62·3
4400	3·30	1·98	7·03	—	2·76	1·71	62·0
4600	3·43	2·19	8·13	—	3·15	1·93	61·3
4800	3·56	2·41	9·37	—	3·57	2·17	60·8
5000	3·70	2·65	$1·08 \times 10^{8}$	—	4·04	2·42	60·0
6000	4·38	4·06	1·98	—	6·87	3·90	56·9
7000	5·12	5·82	3·35	—	$1·08 \times 10^{9}$	$0·58 \times 10^{9}$	53·8
8000	5·90	7·93	5·29	—	1·59	0·80	50·4
9000	6·73	$1·04 \times 10^{-4}$	7·97	—	2·27	1·07	47·2
10000	7·59	1·33	$1·16 \times 10^{9}$	—	3·19	1·45	45·5
11000	8·43	1·62	1·59	—	4·29	1·90	44·3
12000	9·34	2·00	2·19	—	5·80	2·51	43·3
13000	$1·02 \times 10^{5}$	2·39	2·89	—	7·49	3·15	42·0
14000	1·10	2·80	3·69	—	9·39	3·85	41·0
15000	1·19	3·25	4·62	—	$1·15 \times 10^{10}$	$0·46 \times 10^{10}$	40·0
16000	1·27	3·73	5·70	—	1·39	0·54	38·8
17000	1·35	4·20	6·82	—	1·64	0·62	37·8
18000	1·43	4·68	8·07	—	1·90	0·69	36·3
19000	1·51	5·17	9·44	—	2·18	0·76	34·8
20000	1·58	5·62	$1·08 \times 10^{10}$	—	2·46	0·84	34·1
21000	1·66	6·09	1·23	—	2·76	0·91	33·0
22000	1·76	6·62	1·47	—	3·12	0·91	29·1

Note: $\bar{k}_0$ = mass absorption coefficient, E_0 = total internal energy per unit volume, I_0 = ionization energy per unit volume. From z = 22,000 km down to the bottom of the convection zone (z = 63,000 km) a polytropic representation is used. The level z = 300 km corresponds to τ = 0·03, while τ = 1 corresponds to z = 513 km. The upper boundary of the convection zone is located at z = 505 km.

where the subscript zero indicates a mean value taken over a horizontal plane and the asterisk indicates a small local deviation from the mean value. The mean values of the horizontal and vertical velocity components u_0, v_0, and w_0 are taken to be zero. Equations (4.23) and (4.24) then reduce to the following linearized forms:

$$\rho_0 \frac{\partial u}{\partial t} = -\frac{\partial p}{\partial x} \tag{4.28}$$

$$\rho_0 \frac{\partial v}{\partial t} = -\frac{\partial p}{\partial y} \tag{4.29}$$

$$\rho_0 \frac{\partial w}{\partial t} = -\frac{\partial p}{\partial z} + \rho g \tag{4.30}$$

$$\frac{\partial \rho}{\partial t} + \rho_0 \left(\frac{\partial u}{\partial x} + \frac{\partial v}{\partial y} + \frac{\partial w}{\partial z} \right) + \frac{\partial \rho_0}{\partial z} w = 0, \tag{4.31}$$

the asterisks being omitted for convenience.

The linearization of the energy equation (4.25) is more difficult and we shall only quote the result:

$$\rho_0 \frac{\partial E_m}{\partial t} - \frac{p_0}{\rho_0} \frac{\partial \rho}{\partial t} + \rho_0 \frac{\partial E_{m,0}}{\partial z} w - \frac{p_0}{\rho_0} \frac{\partial \rho_0}{\partial z} w$$

$$= \frac{16\sigma}{3} \operatorname{div} \frac{T_0{}^3}{\bar{k}_0 \rho_0} \left[\left(\frac{3T}{T_0} - \frac{\rho}{\rho_0} - \frac{\bar{k}}{\bar{k}_0} \right) \operatorname{grad} T_0 + \operatorname{grad} T \right]. \tag{4.32}$$

Equations (4.28)–(4.32), supplemented by the equation of state, an auxiliary equation derived from (4.32), and the relation

$$\bar{k} = \bar{k}(\rho, T)$$

derived in tabular form from the model, constitute a system of linear partial differential equations which have to be solved simultaneously. As in Rayleigh's classical treatment (Section 4.2.1) one seeks solutions of the form

$$q(x, y, z, t) = Q(z) \exp nt \exp i(k_x x + k_y y), \tag{4.33}$$

where q stands for any one of the dependent variables u, v, w, ρ, or T; n is the growth rate; and k_x and k_y are the wave-numbers in the x- and y-directions. When (4.33) is introduced into (4.28)–(4.32), the equations reduce to a system of ordinary differential equations depending only on z. After the introduction of appropriate boundary conditions and a considerable amount of manipulation, Böhm obtains numerical solutions of the equations, from which he then calculates (*a*) the growth rate n as a function of $K = \sqrt{(k_x^2 + k_y^2)}$; (*b*) the vertical and horizontal velocities as functions of z; and (*c*) the pressure perturbation as a function of z.

The first of these is shown in Fig. 4.2 in the form of a double logarithmic plot; the abscissa axes show both K and the horizontal wavelength $\lambda = 2\pi/K$. The calculated values of n are restricted to horizontal wavelengths lying between 1000 and 100,000 km. n shows a steady increase with K; at $K = 2 \times 10^{-8}$ cm^{-1}, i.e. at $\lambda = 3100$ km, the rate of increase begins to diminish, but it is clear that even at $\lambda = 1000$ km we have not yet reached the maximum value of n, let alone the decrease due to radiative smoothing which must ultimately occur at sufficiently small values of λ. Recalling from Section 2.2.3 that the mean cell size of the granulation is 1800 km, we therefore arrive at the disappointing result that, as in the case of the various

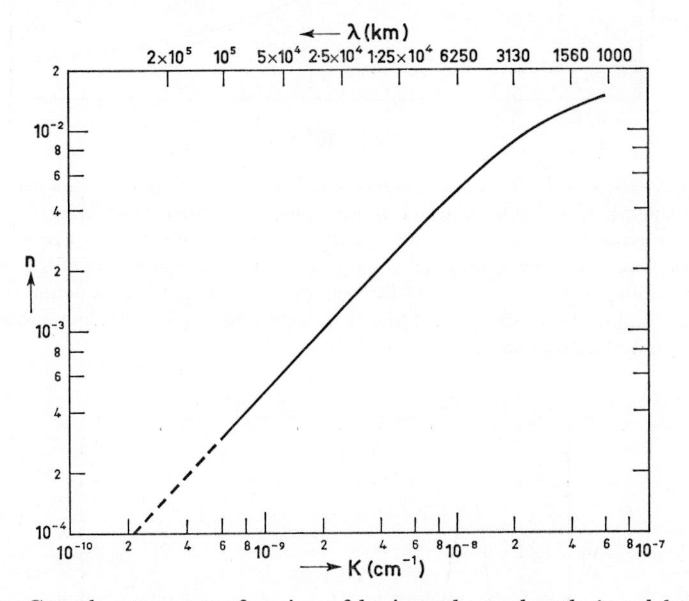

Fig. 4.2. Growth rate n as a function of horizontal wavelength λ and horizontal wave-number K according to a linearized theory of the solar convection zone [Böhm, 1963a]. The dashed portion of the curve is extrapolated. Note that n increases monotonically with K.

treatments based on polytropic atmospheres, Böhm's growth-rate curve yields no maximum that can be identified with the dominant scale of the observed granulation pattern. In passing, we should point out that n in Fig. 4.2 increases much more rapidly with K than in the case of a polytropic atmosphere, essentially owing to the rapid increase in temperature in a thin layer just below the photosphere: for a polytropic atmosphere the temperature increases only linearly with depth (equation (4.22)).

The vertical velocity w is plotted as a function of geometrical depth z in Figs. 4.3–4.4 and 4.5–4.6 for z ranging from 0 to 5000 km and 0 to 800 km respectively. Figure 4.3 gives the velocity for modes with a horizontal wavelength λ of 25,000 km; Fig. 4.4 refers to a wavelength of 1600 km, a figure

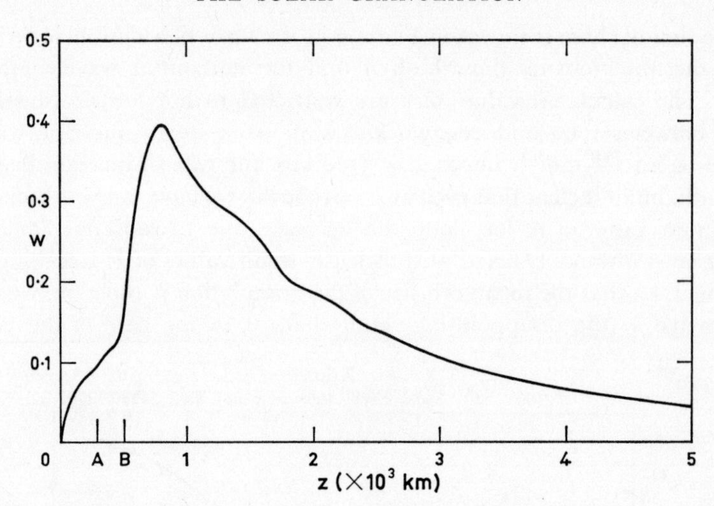

Fig. 4.3. Vertical velocity w (arbitrary units) as a function of geometrical depth [Böhm, 1963a]. The point marked B indicates the upper boundary of the solar convection zone ($\tau \simeq 1$, $z = 505$ km), while A corresponds to the assumed lower boundary of the isothermal layer ($\tau = 0{\cdot}03$). Note the concentration of the velocities towards a thin layer near the top of the convection zone, and their penetration into the stable photosphere above B. This curve refers to a mode having a horizontal wavelength λ of 25,000 km.

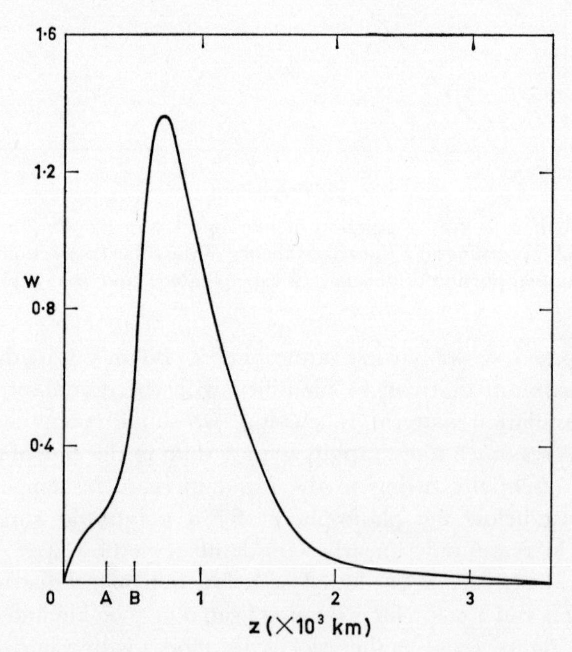

Fig. 4.4. The same as Fig. 4.3, but for a horizontal wavelength of $\lambda = 1600$ km; w is in arbitrary units.

slightly smaller than the mean cell size of the photospheric granulation. The point marked A corresponds to an optical depth of 0.03, the assumed lower boundary of the isothermal layer, while B indicates the upper boundary of the convection zone ($\tau \simeq 1$, $z = 505$ km).

We see immediately from Figs. 4.3 and 4.4 that the vertical velocities are

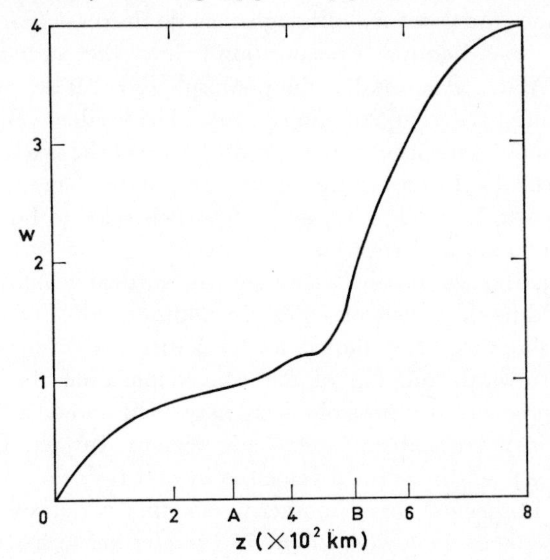

Fig. 4.5. The same as Fig. 4.3, but shown on an expanded z-scale. w is in arbitrary units; $\lambda = 25{,}000$ km.

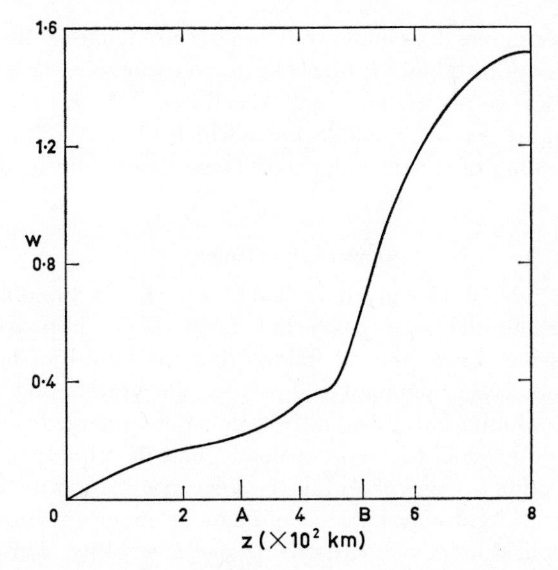

Fig. 4.6. The same as Fig. 4.4, but shown on an expanded z-scale. w is in arbitrary units; $\lambda = 1600$ km.

strongly concentrated towards a thin layer near the top of the convection zone. Moreover, the concentration is more marked for the mode with the smaller horizontal wavelength. This has the consequence that all modes tend to have vertical scales not too different from their horizontal scales.[7]

Secondly, we notice that the velocities do not go to zero at the top of the convection zone (the point B), although they do decrease sharply there. On the contrary, overshooting ('penetration') into the stable photosphere takes place. (Above $z = 505$ km the photosphere is 'stable' in the sense of the Schwarzschild criterion, equation (4.12).) The vertical velocities become equal to zero only at the level $z = 0$, i.e. at the top of the assumed isothermal zone. The vertical velocities in the convectively stable regions are shown on an expanded z-scale in Figs. 4.5 and 4.6, which refer to horizontal wavelengths of 25,000 km and 1600 km respectively.

Figures 2, 3, and 4 of Böhm's paper give the vertical velocity distributions for several additional values of λ and, in addition, plots of the horizontal velocity distributions. The horizontal velocities are even more sharply concentrated towards the top of the convection zone than the vertical velocities. Moreover, the horizontal velocity field shows a more marked overshooting into the stable photospheric regions. In fact, the horizontal velocities differ from the vertical velocities in that they do *not* go to zero at the top of the isothermal zone: in other words, they penetrate right through to the chromosphere. Following Böhm, it is interesting to speculate whether the overshooting of the horizontal velocity field into the chromosphere is related (for the larger wavelengths) to the observed supergranulation (cf. Section 4.5.3).

This completes our description of Böhm's hydrodynamic discussion of the possible modes of instability in the solar convection zone. It is clear that in spite of its failure to predict the observed cell size of the granulation, Böhm's analysis contains several valuable ideas which, in a qualitative way, aid our understanding of the phenomenon. These aspects are further discussed in Section 4.5.

4.3.3 LIMITATIONS OF LINEARIZED THEORY

Let us accept the model given in Table 4.3 as a reasonable zero-order approximation to the solar convection zone. If we also accept Böhm's neglect of viscous forces, then it follows that the failure of his analysis to predict the observed dominant cell size of the granulation can only be ascribed to the limitations inherent in a linear treatment. In order to show how far the linear theory falls short of an adequate description of the phenomenon of convection in general and of the solar granulation in particular, we conclude this section by listing some of its more important limitations:

(1) it is applicable only to cases of *marginal* instability. This implies that

[7] Bearing in mind, of course, that we are here considering only fundamental, not harmonic, modes.

the Rayleigh number R only slightly exceeds R_{crit} or, alternatively, that the disturbances in ρ, p, T, etc., are of infinitesimal amplitude;

(2) it assumes an *exponential* growth rate for all modes (cf. equation (4.33)), whereas what is required are finite, steady-state solutions;

(3) it ignores all coupling, and hence energy exchanges, between the various modes. Therefore, for example, it cannot give the eddy viscosity, and hence the value of the Rayleigh number (Section 4.2.2);

(4) it fails, in the case of the photospheric granulation, to give the relative importance of modes having different scales, i.e. the observed distribution of cell sizes;

(5) it also cannot give the *shape* of the cells, nor the streamlines of the motion nor, indeed, the direction of flow within an individual cell;

(6) it cannot explain the mode of evolution of the cells nor give a value for their lifetime;

(7) it does not take into account terms (non-linear terms) which affect the calculated magnitudes of a number of quantities, including the convective heat transfer, the mean temperature gradient, etc.

4.4 Non-Linear Theories of Convection

4.4.1 INTRODUCTION

The above list forcefully demonstrates the limitations of linearized treatments and, at the same time, gives some hint of the increase in our understanding which could be expected to result from their removal. On the other hand, owing to the formidable mathematical difficulties involved, the development of non-linear theory is still in its infancy, particularly in its application to the interpretation of the solar granulation. In the following section, therefore, we shall confine ourselves merely to outlining a few highlights of modern non-linear treatments which illustrate some of the progress achieved to date. The results of laboratory experiments having a bearing on the modern theoretical developments are briefly discussed in Section 4.4.3.

4.4.2 HIGHLIGHTS OF MODERN NON-LINEAR TREATMENTS

Two interesting questions upon which non-linear theory is capable of throwing some light are: (*a*) how is the mean temperature gradient in the fluid modified as R/R_{crit} steadily becomes greater than unity? and (*b*) what is the detailed temperature distribution inside the individual convection cells? These questions were answered by Kuo [1961] for the case of an infinite, incompressible, convection roll in the steady state.

Starting with the usual basic equations of continuity, momentum, and energy for an incompressible fluid and taking the axis of the roll parallel to the y-axis, Kuo introduces a stream function ψ to represent the motion, given by

$$u = -\frac{\partial \psi}{\partial z}, \quad w = \frac{\partial \psi}{\partial x}. \tag{4.34}$$

The next step is to reduce the basic equations to non-dimensional form. This is carried out by choosing as units of length, time, and temperature, respectively, the quantities

$$h,\ h^2/\kappa,\ \text{and}\ \kappa\nu/g\alpha h^3,$$

where all symbols have the meanings assigned to them in Section 4.2.1 and Table 4.1. If θ represents the difference between the actual temperature and the undisturbed mean temperature (in non-dimensional units), the basic equations then reduce to a closed system of two non-linear differential equations for the two dependent variables ψ and θ, namely

$$\nabla^4\psi + \frac{\partial\theta}{\partial x} = \frac{1}{\sigma^*}\frac{\partial(\psi, \nabla^2\psi)}{\partial(x, z)} \tag{4.35}$$

and

$$\nabla^2\theta + R\frac{\partial\psi}{\partial x} = \frac{\partial(\psi, \theta)}{\partial(x, z)}. \tag{4.36}$$

In the steady-state vorticity equation (4.35), the Jacobian $\partial(\psi, \nabla^2\psi)/\partial(x, z)$ is termed the 'vorticity advection' and σ^* is the Prandtl number ν/κ. In the thermal energy equation (4.36), the Jacobian $\partial(\psi,\theta)/\partial(x,z)$ is termed the 'heat advection' and R is the Rayleigh number $g\alpha\Delta Th^3/\kappa\nu$.

Equations (4.35) and (4.36) are solved by assuming solutions in the form of double Fourier expansions, viz.:

$$\left.\begin{aligned} \psi &= \sum_{l=0}^{\infty}\sum_{m=0}^{\infty} \psi_{l,m} \sin lK_{1,1}\pi x \,.\, \sin m\pi z \\ \theta &= \sum_{l=0}^{\infty}\sum_{m=0}^{\infty} \theta_{l,m} \cos lK_{1,1}\pi x \,.\, \sin m\pi z \end{aligned}\right\} \tag{4.37}$$

In these equations l and m are integers and $\pi K_{1,1}$ is the horizontal wave-number of the first mode ($l = m = 1$). Since convection is assumed to occur when R reaches R_{crit}, which is a function of $K_{1,1}$, one must choose $K_{1,1}$ so as to make R_{crit} a minimum. The minimum value of R_{crit} for the case of two free boundaries is $27\pi^4/4$ (cf. Section 4.2.1). The amplitudes $\psi_{l,m}$ and $\theta_{l,m}$ are functions of R and σ^* as well as l and m.

Each term in the solution (4.37) satisfies appropriate boundary conditions for the case of two free boundaries. This solution may be contrasted with the linear solution given in Section 4.3.2 (equation (4.33)), from which it differs in two respects: (*a*) there is no time-dependent term; and (*b*) all modes, each with its own particular amplitude, are taken to be simultaneously present and to contribute to the fields of motion and temperature variation.

The last step is to determine the amplitudes $\psi_{l,m}$ and $\theta_{l,m}$ in such a way that (4.37) satisfies (4.35) and (4.36). The mathematics is not difficult but is too lengthy to reproduce here, and for details the reader should consult the original paper.

One of the principal aims of Kuo's analysis was to determine how the gradient of the *mean* temperature (i.e. averaged over a horizontal plane) is modified as R exceeds R_{crit} by successively greater amounts. This is shown in Fig. 4.7. In this diagram the ordinate represents height above the lower boundary in units of the layer thickness h, while the abscissa represents the difference between the mean temperature and the temperature of the lower boundary in non-dimensional units. The number beside each curve gives the corresponding value of R/R_{crit}.

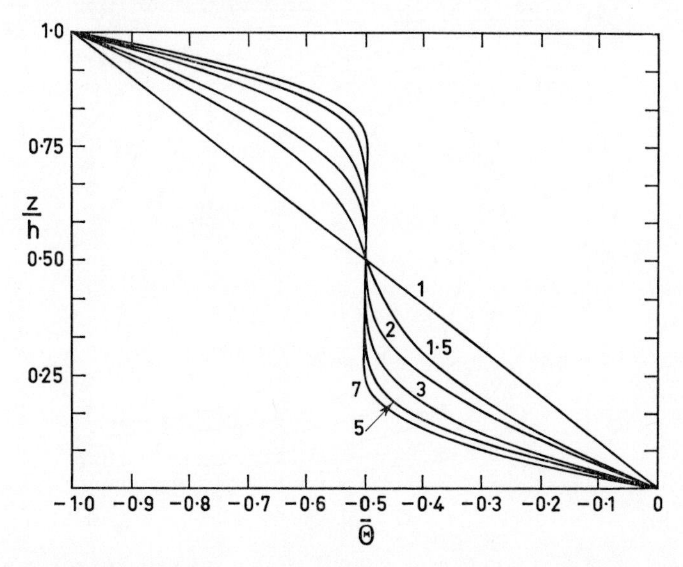

Fig. 4.7. Distribution of mean temperature with depth as a function of R/R_{crit} according to non-linear theory [Kuo, 1961]. Ordinate: height above lower boundary in units of the layer thickness. Abscissa: difference between the horizontally-averaged temperature and the temperature of the lower boundary in non-dimensional units. The number beside each curve gives R/R_{crit}. Note the isothermal region which appears in the middle of the layer as the Rayleigh number R increases beyond 2 R_{crit}. As R/R_{crit} further increases, the large temperature gradients become increasingly confined to thin layers near the upper and lower boundaries.

The outstanding feature shown by this diagram is the isothermal region (adiabatic in the case of a gas) which appears in the middle of the fluid layer as R increases beyond 2 R_{crit}. Moreover, as R is further increased, the thickness of the isothermal layer increases. Hence, for a large imposed temperature difference ΔT, the main body of the fluid is isothermal and large temperature gradients are confined to thin layers near the upper and lower boundaries. This rather paradoxical result is attributed by Kuo to the direct influence of non-linear interactions.

A second interesting result obtained by Kuo is illustrated in Fig. 4.8, which gives the pattern of isotherms of the *actual* temperature for a half-cell for the case $R = 7\,R_{crit}$, $\sigma^* = 10$. It will be noticed that the large temperature gradients are confined to those regions where the ascending currents are approaching the upper boundary and the descending currents are approaching the lower boundary; elsewhere on the boundaries, and also in the main body of the cell, the gradients are small.

It is evident from the above description of Kuo's work that a non-linear analysis is potentially capable of giving extremely detailed results which, indeed, represent quite a challenge to observation and experiment.*

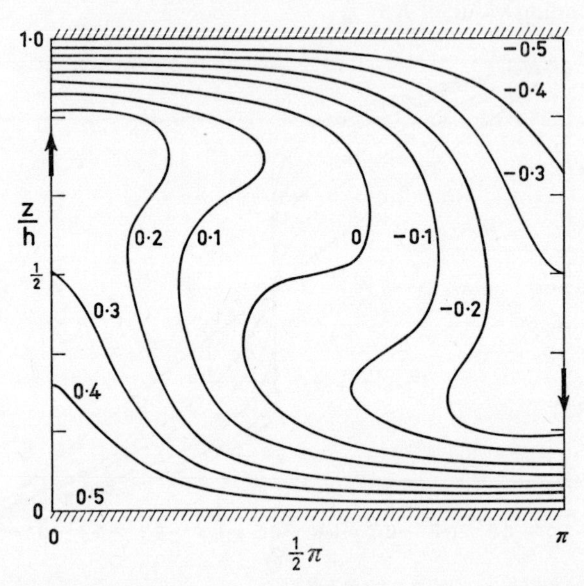

Fig. 4.8. Pattern of isotherms (non-dimensional units) for a half-cell for the case $R = 7\,R_{\text{crit}}$, σ^* (Prandtl number) = 10, according to Kuo's non-linear theory. Note the confinement of the large temperature gradients to those regions where the ascending currents approach the upper boundary and the descending currents approach the lower boundary.

Credit for the first non-linear treatment of convection belongs to Malkus and Veronis [1958]. These authors sought to determine: (*a*) how the convective heat transport depends on the Rayleigh number (a problem also pursued by Kuo in the paper described above); and (*b*) the *preferred shape* of the convection cells. They found that square cells are preferred to hexagonal

* *Note added in the proof.* In a recent paper J. E. Fromm (*Phys. Fluids* **8**, 1757 (1965); Erratum, *Ibid.* **9**, 828 (1966)) has expressed the differential equations of the convection roll problem in a finite difference form and employed a computer to obtain numerical solutions. Fig. 4 of Fromm's paper gives isotherms, streamlines, and isodines (lines of constant vorticity) for values of R ranging from $3\,R_{\text{crit}}$ to $15\,R_{\text{crit}}$ for the free boundaries case, the results being in good accord with Kuo's. Figs. 8 and 9 give the corresponding solutions for the rigid boundaries case for R ranging from 30,000 to 10^7. It is noteworthy that even at such high Rayleigh numbers the streamline patterns continue to indicate laminar flow over nearly the entire cell, although the isotherms and isodines show increasing complexity. Fromm's work represents a powerful attack on the non-linear convection problem and points the way to further progress.

cells if, in selecting the physically realized solutions, the criterion of maximum heat transport is adopted. The question of cell shape was later studied by Palm [1960], also on the basis of non-linear theory. However, in contradiction to Malkus and Veronis, he found that hexagonal cells are preferred, a result supported by Palm and Øiann [1964]. Palm's work was corrected and extended by Segel and Stuart [1962]. These authors concluded that hexagonal cells *may* constitute a stable equilibrium state, but only if the variation of the kinematic viscosity ν with temperature is sufficiently large.

How ν varies with T also determines the *direction of motion* of the convection currents. According to Palm, who again bases his conclusion on non-linear theory, there is ascent or descent in the middle of the cell according to whether ν decreases or increases with T; the first case holds for the majority of liquids and the second for most gases. Palm's conclusion was confirmed by Segel and Stuart and accords with experiment [Stuart, 1964].

Stuart's paper is of particular interest because he uses non-linear theory to calculate not merely the direction of flow but also the actual *streamlines* in a hexagonal convection cell. In addition, he pays careful attention to the question of properly defining the cell boundary in such a way that the 'mathematical' cell corresponds to that actually observed in laboratory experiments. According to Stuart, the cell boundary must satisfy the following conditions: (*a*) no particle of fluid can pass through a cell boundary; and (*b*) the vertical velocity w on a vertical boundary surface must everywhere be of the same sign and cannot equal zero at any point except at the intersections with the two horizontal boundary surfaces. It is implicit in (*a*) that the boundary surfaces contain streamlines.

Actual streamlines for a hexagonal cell are shown schematically in Fig. 4.9. The curve DOA represents two curved projected streamlines OA and OD joining the centre O to two boundary nodes A and D. The curved cylindrical surface of which DOA is the projection is shown as $DOAA'O'D'$; the closed curves with arrows are streamlines lying in this surface. The dotted lines indicate the boundaries of the hexagonal cell, seen in perspective. In this figure, the direction of flow is taken as downward at the cell centre, as in the case of most gases. However, the streamlines would be similar if the flow were upward at the centre, as in most liquids.

Figure 4.10 gives the projection of the streamlines onto the horizontal boundary surface $ABCDEF$. The dashed circle represents the projection of a surface of zero vertical velocity, $w = 0$. Within this surface, material is sinking; outside, it is rising. We note that the boundary surface $ABCDEF$ accords with the definition of the boundary given above, since the streamlines AB, BC, etc., do not intersect the curve $w = 0$. On the other hand, an equilateral triangle whose corners are located at O and at the centres of two adjacent hexagons could *not* constitute an experimentally observable cell because the sides of such a triangle would cut the curves $w = 0$.

Stuart's analysis, like Kuo's investigation described above, gives some idea

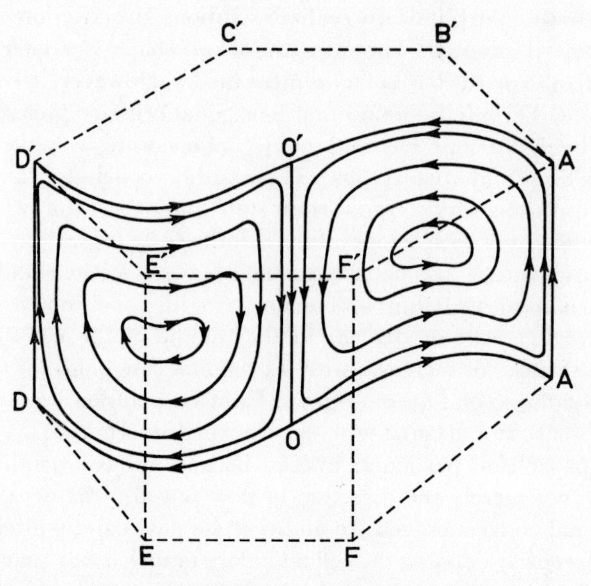

Fig. 4.9. Streamlines in a hexagonal convection cell, according to non-linear theory [Stuart, 1964]. The streamline pattern is similar when the direction of circulation is opposite to that shown, i.e. upward instead of downward at the cell centre.

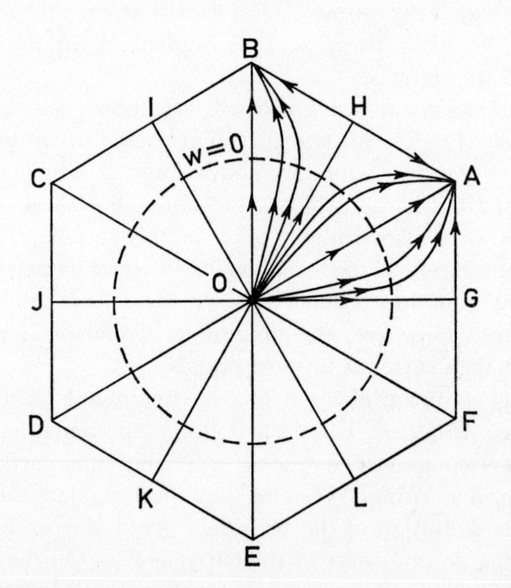

Fig. 4.10. Projection of the streamlines of the hexagonal convection cell of Fig. 4.9 onto the horizontal boundary surface *ABCDEF*. The dashed circle represents the projection of a surface of zero vertical velocity, $w = 0$. Within this surface, material is sinking; outside, it is rising.

of the detailed results which non-linear theory is potentially capable of yielding. However, only a few very tentative attempts have so far been made to apply non-linear theory to the solar convection zone. Kato [1961] and Ledoux, Schwarzschild, and Spiegel [1961] have attempted to calculate the energy exchange between the various modes, Kato giving an expression for the eddy viscosity. However, both analyses are based on the Heisenberg theory of turbulence and thus fail to provide much physical insight into the actual details of the convective processes. More recently, Souffrin [1963] has tried to use turbulence theory to predict the *mode of evolution* of the photospheric granules. Souffrin's analysis is very abstract and hard to follow, and his predictions do not accord with the observations described in Section 2.2.8. Nevertheless, the authors mentioned above deserve full credit for their pioneering attempts at a very difficult task.

4.4.3 LABORATORY EXPERIMENTS ON CELLULAR CONVECTION

Laboratory experiments having much degree of relevance to solar convection and to the interpretation of the granulation are unfortunately few and far between. In the first place, the majority of such experiments have been carried out with liquids rather than with gases. Secondly, recent work has shown that considerable doubt must sometimes be cast on the interpretation of experiments with liquids since in many cases it seems that the observed cellular pattern is due not to buoyancy forces but rather to *surface tension* forces.

Observations show that laminar and steady motion giving a cellular pattern occurs for a surprisingly wide range of values of the Rayleigh number R exceeding R_{crit} [Malkus and Veronis, 1958; Schwarzschild, 1959; Kuo, 1961]. According to Malkus and Veronis, steady cellular convection occurs for values of R up to 10 R_{crit}. Within this range the convective heat transport increases linearly with R, from zero at $R = R_{crit}$ to a value greater than that due to conduction alone at $R = 10\ R_{crit}$. At $R > 10\ R_{crit}$ a new instability appears, producing aperiodic motions, quasi-cellular in appearance. The heat transport continues to increase linearly with R, but with a steeper slope than before. At even higher values of R, further changes occur which further steepen the slope of the heat transport curve. Malkus and Veronis attribute these discontinuities to the emergence of new instabilities; each transition leads to higher velocities and an apparently more disordered pattern. Malkus [1954] has detected no less than six discrete transitions in the slope of the heat transport curve between $R = 1700$ and $R = 10^6$.

According to experiments carried out by Schmidt and Saunders [1938], both water and air become 'completely turbulent' when R reaches a value of 45,000 ($= 26\ R_{crit}$). In the case of water, the turbulence develops suddenly at this value of R, but for air the first signs of disorder appear at about $R =$ 5000 ($= 3\ R_{crit}$). Malkus [1960], on the other hand, finds that for liquids the transition from a quasi-cellular to a fully turbulent pattern is delayed until

$R = 10^6$. Schwarzschild [1959] uses the term 'non-stationary convection' to describe the motion which occurs when $R > 100\ R_{crit}$ and gives references to laboratory investigations of this type of motion, which he tentatively identifies with the photospheric granulation.

Much of the laboratory work on convection has centred on a determination of R_{crit} and its comparison with theory. Most such experiments have been confined to liquids [for references, see Gille and Goody, 1964], but Gille and Goody have measured R_{crit} for a radiating gas (ammonia) and for dry air. This experiment appears to be the first accurate determination of R_{crit} for a gas.

The direction of circulation in a convection cell has already been mentioned in the previous section in connection with non-linear theory. Observation appears to confirm that there is ascent or descent in the middle of the cell according as the kinematic viscosity ν decreases or increases with temperature, the first case corresponding to most liquids, the second to most gases [Malkus and Veronis, 1958; Palm, 1960; Segel and Stuart, 1962; Stuart, 1964].

The question of cell shape does not seem to have received the attention it deserves. In experiments in air, smoke can be used to delineate the cell boundaries; reference to such an experiment, in which hexagonal cells were observed, has been made by Stuart [1964]. Stuart also describes experiments with liquids in which an optical method of showing the cells is employed. References to earlier observations, including those of Bénard, are given by Rayleigh [1916], Wasiutynski [1946], and Scriven and Sternling [1964].

Scriven and Sternling's paper is of special interest in that it contains a severe but convincing criticism of the commonly-accepted interpretation of Bénard cells in terms of buoyancy-driven convection. Instead, they contend that in many such experiments *surface tension* forces provide the driving mechanism. They remark that convective-type motions have been observed to occur at much lower Rayleigh numbers than theory predicts – and even in a layer of liquid *cooled* from below! In addition, drying paint films often display Bénard-type cells: when they do, the circulation is observed to continue whether the free surface is on the underside or topside of the layer and therefore cannot be due to buoyancy forces. Scriven and Sternling conclude that such cells are produced by variations in surface tension due to non-uniformities in temperature over the free surface, and they proceed to formulate a theory of the effect on this basis. Nield [1964] has independently arrived at similar conclusions.

In cellular flow driven by surface tension, there is upflow beneath depressions of the free surface and downflow beneath elevations; in buoyancy-driven convection the converse holds. This provides a simple observational means of distinguishing which of the two mechanisms is dominant in any given case. When there is no free surface, buoyancy must of course be the sole agency responsible.

In conclusion, it should be emphasized that there is a great need for more laboratory experiments having a greater relevance to the problem of convection in the Sun. Such experiments should preferably be carried out with gases; if liquids are employed, both boundaries should be rigid in order to avoid surface tension effects. In both cases the Rayleigh number should be allowed to range very widely, reaching values of at least, say, 10^5–10^6, and perhaps even beyond.

4.5 Interpretation of Observed Properties of the Granulation and Supergranulation

4.5.1 INTRODUCTION

In the previous sections of this chapter we have tried to give an account of theoretical work on convection (together with the somewhat meagre experimental results) having some degree of relevance to the problem of the interpretation of the granulation. We have not hitherto, however, discussed the theory of convection in relation to the actual observed features of the granulation, which are exhaustively described in Chapters 2 and 3. This we now propose to do, dealing with the photospheric granulation in Section 4.5.2 and the supergranulation in Section 4.5.3.

Before proceeding to discuss individual observational features, it is important to clearly state the main reasons for regarding the granulation as a convective phenomenon. These reasons are threefold, the first two being based on observational evidence and the third being inferred from our 'zero-order' knowledge of the physical conditions in the solar convection zone:

(1) the granulation shows a clearly-defined cellular pattern with a relatively narrow distribution of cell sizes (Sections 2.1 and 2.2.3). Buoyancy-driven convection is the only physical mechanism known to produce such a pattern, apart from surface tension and other agencies known to be absent;

(2) there is a strong correlation in *sense* between brightness and velocity in the photosphere, about 70 per cent of the bright features visible in the continua of spectrograms showing violet Doppler shifts and 70 per cent of the dark features showing red shifts (Sections 2.4.1 and 2.4.3). This is qualitatively what one would expect for buoyancy-driven convection, since the hot gases must move upward;

(3) if the granulation is to be identified as a convective phenomenon, then we must find a source of energy for driving the convective motions. It is now generally agreed that this source is the *liberation of hydrogen ionization energy* by upward-moving material. The effect is very clearly seen in Table 4.3, the last column of which gives the ionization energy of hydrogen and helium as a percentage of the total energy (thermal + ionization). It will be noticed that except in the top few hundred kilometres, the ionization energy I_0 – mainly due to hydrogen – is a substantial fraction of the total energy, amounting to no less than 67 per cent throughout the range $z = 1300$ km

to $z = 2400$ km. At $z = 700$ km, I_0 has declined to just under 50 per cent of the total energy, but it is in the next 200 km that the most dramatic decrease occurs: at $z = 500$ km, I_0 has dropped to a mere 0·6 per cent of the total as a result of the almost complete re-combination of the hydrogen ions. If we imagine an elementary volume of gas moving upwards through such a region of decreasing ionization, then it is clear that as it moves upwards it liberates ionization energy. This in turn is converted to thermal energy. Thus the buoyancy of the element is increased and it continues its upward journey, provided the forces opposing its motion are sufficiently small. In other words, the medium is convectively unstable. The instability is very high when, as here, the degree of ionization changes very rapidly with depth.

These are the main reasons, therefore, which lead us to identify the photospheric granulation with cellular convection, the driving force owing its origin to the release of hydrogen ionization energy a few hundred kilometres below the photosphere.

This view is now generally, although not universally, accepted [see, for example, Leighton, 1963; Simon and Leighton, 1964]. On the other hand, Plaskett [1955, 1963], while accepting the release of ionization energy as a cause of convective instability, believes that the granulation is actually due to the presence of a steep temperature gradient in the photosphere produced by *boundary cooling*; he points out that the granulation is observed in a zone where there is *no* hydrogen ionization. Accordingly, he does not believe that the granulation can supply observational checks of the theory of the hydrogen convection zone. We do not agree with this view which, among other things, takes no account of the phenomenon of *penetration*, discussed below.[8]

E. A. Spiegel [1964b] has also sought alternative explanations. He makes the interesting suggestion that rather than being thermally generated, the granulation may be mechanically driven by the supergranulation; however, no detailed theory of such a process has yet been worked out. Both Plaskett and Spiegel take the view that the supergranulation is a manifestation of motions in the hydrogen convection zone. The interpretation of the supergranulation is discussed in more detail below (Section 4.5.3).

In the following section, we shall examine to what extent some of the detailed properties of the granulation can be interpreted in the light of the theoretical knowledge outlined in the previous sections.

4.5.2 THE PHOTOSPHERIC GRANULATION

(1) *Mean cell size.* The granulation pattern has a well-defined and rather narrow distribution of cell sizes (Fig. 2.1), the mean value being 1800 km (Section 2.2.3). In contradiction to this result, linearized theory, as we have seen in Section 4.3, gives a growth-rate curve that shows *no* maximum that can be identified with the peak of the observed cell size distribution. Spiegel

[8] In an earlier paper, Plaskett [1936] expressed views substantially the same as those adopted by us.

[1964a,b] has sought to explain this discrepancy by the suggestion that in the upper layers of the convection zone, where the granulation is observed, certain factors operate to reduce the amplitudes of the small-scale disturbances: therefore, these modes are not observed and the peak in the distribution curve is restored. However, a full explanation of the observed mean cell size and of the observed distribution of cell sizes lies within the realm of non-linear theory.

It is of some interest to calculate the ratio $Q = \lambda/h$, where λ is the mean cell size and h is the effective thickness of the convecting layer. We may take the upper boundary of the layer to be located at $\tau \simeq 1$ (cf. Section 4.3.2), since at this level the convecting elements begin to radiate away to outer space a substantial fraction of their thermal energy; $\tau = 1$ corresponds to $z \simeq 500$ km in Table 4.3. The lower boundary is not so well determined; however, examination of the last column of Table 4.3 shows that the ionization energy, as a percentage of the total energy, begins to undergo a marked decline in the region $z = 800$–900 km. This gives a value of h of about 350 km, and with $\lambda = 1800$ km, we thus obtain $Q \simeq 5$.

According to Simon and Leighton [1964], a value of Q ranging from 5 to 10 is characteristic of 'non-stationary' convection observed in nature over a very wide range of densities and cell sizes. As an example, they cite Tiros photographs showing convection patterns in cloud formations for which $Q = 10$. Weiss [1964] has shown that in the case of an incompressible fluid having equal vertical and horizontal velocities, continuity considerations require that $Q = 4$. The value for Q in the classical Rayleigh problem is 2–3, depending on the boundary conditions, a value confirmed by experiments on air and water carried out by Schmidt and Saunders [1938]. However, it is not certain how much significance should be attached to the fairly good agreement between these figures and the value for the granulation; for one thing, it is clearly rather an over-simplification to regard the ionization energy of the rising material as being liberated in a sharply defined layer.

(2) *Lifetime.* One might expect the observed lifetime to be equal to or greater than the time t required for a particle to make a complete journey around a convection cell. A simple calculation, however, shows that this is *not* so: taking a velocity of 0·2 km/sec (Section 2.4), and assuming that the velocity remains constant around the entire path,[9] we have

$$t = \frac{2 \times 350 + 2 \times \frac{1}{2} \times 1800}{0{\cdot}2} = 1{\cdot}25 \times 10^4 \text{ sec} \simeq 200 \text{ min.}$$

This figure is over an order of magnitude greater than the observed lifetime of 10 min (Section 2.2.7).

How are we to explain this large discrepancy? Part of it may be due to the possibility that the actual velocity in the streamlines – whose measurement

[9] Actually, continuity considerations require the velocity to be smaller at the bottom of the cell, since the density there is greater.

is beyond existing capability – may be much larger than the value 0·2 km/sec quoted above. If so, the latter figure represents some sort of averaged value.

A second possibility is that the granules, notwithstanding their cellular appearance, actually represent convective *plumes* rather than cells. (This possibility has been mentioned by Simon and Leighton [1964] in connection with the supergranulation.) In this case, the travel distance is reduced to 350 km and t becomes 30 min. This type of convection is well known in meteorology [see, for example, Priestley, 1959]. On the other hand, the cellular appearance of the photospheric granulation would seem to be against such an interpretation.

Once again, it is likely that only non-linear theory can properly account for the observed lifetime of the granules. This applies with even more emphasis to explaining their modes of evolution (Section 2.2.8).

(3) *Granulation near the extreme limb: height of penetration.* The granulation has been observed up to a distance of 5″ of arc from the limb, implying that the granules extend upwards at least as high as optical depth $\tau = 0{\cdot}1$ (Section 2.3). Since the upper boundary of the convection zone is located at $\tau \simeq 1$, the observations therefore show that the *convective motions responsible for the granulation penetrate deeply into the stable layers.* This conclusion is entirely consistent with Böhm's analysis which, on the basis of linear theory, shows that the vertical velocities, although concentrated near the top of the convection zone, penetrate into the stable photosphere (Section 4.3.2 and Figs. 4.3 and 4.4).

According to Veronis [1963], penetration into stably-stratified regions ordinarily occurs in natural convection. He cites two examples of penetrative convection in the field of geophysics, namely convection in the Earth's atmosphere and convection at the surface of the oceans. The depth of penetration depends on the viscosity [Spiegel, 1964b].

(4) *The oscillatory velocity field.* Observations made in both weak and strong lines (Sections 2.4.2 and 2.4.3) reveal the presence around the level $\tau = 0{\cdot}1$, and in the chromosphere above, of oscillatory velocities having periods of about 5 min and a scale comparable with that of the granulation. At any given location, the oscillations seem to persist for upwards of three full periods, i.e. 15 min. Although further observations are needed to establish the exact relationship between the small velocity regions and the granules themselves, it seems likely that each penetrating convection current (see above) behaves as a piston, exciting oscillations, perhaps of the resonance type, in the overlying atmosphere. In this way a mechanism is provided for transporting energy from the convection zone up into the chromosphere, and perhaps even into the corona. It may not be too much of an over-simplification to describe the whole mechanism as convection – penetration – oscillation – dissipation, each hydrodynamic process occupying a certain range of depths. However, the general problem of the heating and structure of the chromosphere and corona lies beyond the scope of this book and for detailed

discussions the reader should refer to review articles by van de Hulst [1953], Pagel [1964], and Kuperus [1965].

(5) *Direction of cellular motion.* In gaseous convection in the laboratory, the direction of circulation in a cell appears to be such that the fluid moves downward at the centre of the cell and upward at the cell boundary (Section 4.4.3). Moreover, this pattern of circulation, which is illustrated in Fig. 4.9, agrees with the predictions of non-linear theory (Section 4.4.2). On the other hand, the direction of circulation in a photospheric granule is evidently just the opposite to that shown in Fig. 4.9, since we observe bright material (upward-moving) surrounded by dark material (downward-moving). If the circulation were the same as in Fig. 4.9, we would evidently observe narrow bright lanes of intergranular material surrounding dark granules! The latter direction of circulation would appear to provide an equally effective convective mechanism, and it is hard to find a simple reason why it does *not* occur. Presumably the answer is to be found in a full non-linear treatment which takes into account both the high density gradient and radiative effects including, in particular, uncompensated radiation losses from hot rising material at the top of the convection zone ($\tau \simeq 1$).

If we can assume that eddy viscosity plays an analogous rôle to atomic viscosity in determining the direction of flow, then the observed direction of circulation in the granules evidently implies that the eddy viscosity decreases with depth.

Detailed velocity measurements across a single granule would go a long way towards increasing our understanding of the circulation in the corresponding convection cell or, alternatively, of deciding whether or not it may rather be a question of a plume-like structure. With a spatial resolution of 0″.4 of arc, corresponding to the theoretical resolution of a 12-inch telescope, it would be possible to measure the velocity at five positions across a large granule having a foreshortened diameter of, say, 2″. Such measurements are beyond existing techniques, but some of the instrumental developments described in Chapter 5 may soon bring them within the realm of possibility.

To conclude this section, we should emphasize once again that the interpretation of many of the observed features of the granulation lies within the scope of non-linear theory, whose application to the solar convection zone is unfortunately still in its infancy. In this section we have tried to confront existing theoretical ideas with just a few of the basic observational facts. The interpretation of other observed features, such as granule shape, evolution, diversity in brightness, etc., must await the development of an adequate non-linear theory of solar convection.

4.5.3 THE SUPERGRANULATION

As we have seen in Section 3.4, the supergranulation consists of a system of relatively well-ordered and long-lived convective motions which can be likened to a larger-scale version of the familiar photospheric granulation.

The ordinary granulation owes its origin to the highly unstable zone located a few hundred kilometres below the bottom of the photosphere, where a high degree of instability is brought about by hydrogen de-ionization (Section 4.5.1). Arguing by analogy, it does not seem unreasonable to identify the supergranulation with portion of the weakly unstable region which, according to Böhm-Vitense's model, has its lower boundary at a depth of 63,000 km. This identification receives some support from Böhm's hydrodynamic discussion of the convection zone (Section 4.3.2), which shows a strong overshooting of the horizontal velocity field through the stable portion of the photosphere into the chromosphere above.[10]

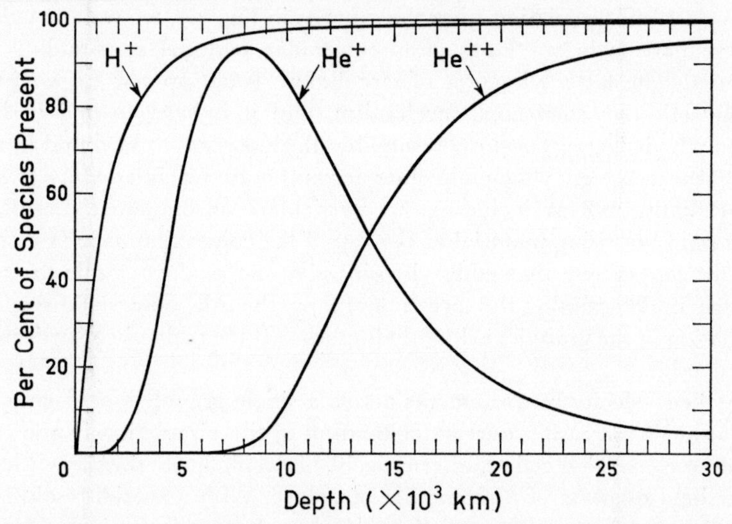

Fig. 4.11. Ionization of hydrogen and helium in the solar convection zone according to unpublished data of Iben and Sears [Simon and Leighton, 1964]. The photospheric granulation is attributed to the release of ionization energy by hydrogen, the supergranulation to the release of ionization energy by singly- and doubly-ionized helium (see text). In this diagram, zero depth corresponds to $\tau = 0{\cdot}67$.

Let us see what value we obtain for the effective layer thickness h if we apply the formula $Q = \lambda/h$ already used for the photospheric granulation (Section 4.5.2). Taking Q to be 5 – the value obtained for the photospheric granulation – and the cell size λ to be 35,000 km (Section 3.4), we have

$$h = 35{,}000/5 = 7000 \text{ km}.$$

What possible mechanism selects a cell depth of roughly 7000 km? Simon and Leighton [1964] have suggested that the mechanism responsible may be the *ionization of neutral or singly-ionized helium, or perhaps both.*[11] This suggestion receives considerable support from Fig. 4.11, which shows the percentage

[10] On the other hand, as in the case of the photospheric granulation, Böhm's analysis fails to predict the dominant scale of the supergranulation.

[11] The importance of helium ionization in determining the structure of convection zones has been pointed out by other authors, including Böhm-Vitense [1958] and Pecker [1959].

ionizations of hydrogen, helium, and singly-ionized helium as a function of geometrical depth, according to unpublished calculations of I. Iben and R. Sears. We notice from Fig. 4.11 that 50 per cent of the neutral helium becomes singly ionized at a depth of about 4000 km, while 50 per cent of the helium becomes doubly ionized at about 14,000 km. (Single and double ionization commence at 2000 and 7000 km respectively.) Between the depths 4000 and 14,000 km, therefore, there is a liberation of ionization energy by upward-moving material due to the re-combination with electrons of singly- and doubly-ionized helium atoms. The calculated effective layer depth of about 7000 km for the supergranulation lies well within this range.

There are two intriguing features of the supergranulation which call for special comment:

(1) the supergranulation is observable only as a *velocity* pattern, and not as an *intensity* pattern. This implies that the corresponding thermal energy convected to the surface is much smaller than in the case of the photospheric granulation. This in turn may be a consequence of the much smaller ionization energy involved, since helium is only about 1/10th as abundant as hydrogen;

(2) even the best photographs of the photospheric granulation give no evidence of any distorting effects which could be attributed to the horizontal velocities associated with the supergranulation. For example, one might expect to see the granules more closely packed towards the boundaries of the supergranules, with a corresponding thinning-out at their centres. This, however, is not observed: although there are occasional variations in the packing of the granules from place to place, these variations appear to occur at random (cf. Section 2.2.4).

It remains now to ask what effects, if any, are produced by the remaining portion of the weakly unstable region which, according to Böhm-Vitense's zero-order model of the convection zone, extends down to 63,000 km. Here we can only speculate. Perhaps beneath the supergranule cells there are stacked a series of additional cells, each having a depth comparable with the local scale height – thus allowing the continuity equation to be satisfied without a marked variation in velocity between top and bottom [Weiss, 1964] – the series as a whole extending all the way to the bottom of the convection zone.[12] Perhaps this region manifests itself at the photospheric level in motions having a horizontal scale even larger than that of the supergranulation, but not yet observed or identified.

4.6 Inhomogeneous Photospheric Models and Non-Uniform Radiative Transfer

4.6.1 INTRODUCTION

Amongst other shortcomings, the zero-order model of the solar convection zone given in Table 4.3 departs from reality in one very important respect:

[12] Böhm [1963b] has calculated growth rates for such harmonic modes, using linear theory and Böhm-Vitense's model.

it gives no expression to horizontal variations in such physical quantities as the temperature, density, pressure, absorption coefficient, etc., although the very existence of the photospheric granulation implies that such variations must be present. Obviously, there are two basic reasons for developing an inhomogeneous model of the solar photosphere and the convection zone as a whole: (*a*) only an inhomogeneous model of the photosphere can provide a proper theoretical basis for explaining, on the one hand, the observed values of such quantities as the granular contrast and its centre-limb variation and, on the other hand, the asymmetry in the profiles of Fraunhofer lines and the centre-limb variation of their wavelengths; (*b*) only an inhomogeneous model of the convection zone, together with an appropriate radiative transfer theory applicable to non-uniform media, can give the exact form of the radiative term or terms which, as we have seen in Section 4.3.1, have to be included in the basic hydrodynamic equations governing astrophysical convection.

However, only in the last decade have any serious attempts been made to include the inhomogeneity of the solar atmosphere in theoretical discussions of the various observations.[13] Moreover, even the most recent inhomogeneous models must be regarded as extremely tentative, and any detailed numerical results should be viewed with great caution. In the following sections we shall briefly describe these pioneering attempts, dealing first with inhomogeneous models based on observations of Fraunhofer lines (Section 4.6.2) and then with the application of non-uniform radiative transfer theory to observations made in integrated radiation (Section 4.6.3).

4.6.2 INHOMOGENEOUS MODELS BASED ON OBSERVATIONS OF FRAUNHOFER LINES

One way in which the inhomogeneity of the photosphere can influence a Fraunhofer line is by making the line profile *asymmetrical*. The origin of the asymmetry is easy to understand. Let us assume, for simplicity, a 'two-stream' model of the region of line formation, i.e. one with alternate columns of hot upward-moving and cold downward-moving material. The spatial resolution usually attained in spectroscopic observations is such that in most cases the profiles corresponding to the hot and cold elements cannot be separated; the profile recorded on a spectrogram is then a superposition of the two profiles, each shifted by an amount corresponding to its Doppler velocity. If the 'hot' and 'cold' profiles were identical, no asymmetry would result, only a broadening. In general, however, this will not be so: e.g., for lines of high excitation and ionization potentials, the 'hot' profile will certainly be stronger than the 'cold' [Voigt, 1956]. In such a case it is clear that their superposition will produce an asymmetrical profile whose violet

[13] References to earlier attempts have been given by Böhm [1954b], who himself applied an inhomogeneous model to the calculation of the centre-limb variation of certain line profiles; see also de Jager [1959: pp. 86–92].

side will be more extensive than its red side. The magnitude of the asymmetry can conveniently be measured by the quantity

$$A = \frac{h_v - h_r}{h_v + h_r},$$

where h_v and h_r have the meanings indicated in Fig. 4.12.

Measurements of the asymmetries of three particularly suitable lines, the infra-red oxygen triplet $\lambda\lambda$7772, 7774, and 7775, have been made by Voigt [1956]. He found that the value of A for these lines, expressed as a percentage, varied from about 9 per cent at the centre of the solar disk to zero at the limb. Voigt used these observations to derive a 'three-stream' model of the photosphere, taking as his starting point Böhm's [1954a] non-grey radiative equilibrium model and assuming, among other things, that the lines in question are formed by true absorption.

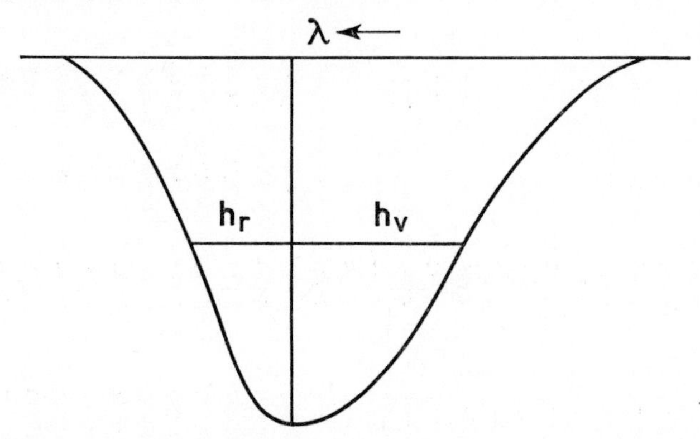

Fig. 4.12. Asymmetry of Fraunhofer line (schematic); h_v and h_r are measured at the half-intensity point.

However, in view of the possible presence of unknown blending lines, great care must be exercised in interpreting observations of line asymmetry. For example, in a second paper Voigt [1959] found that the infra-red nickel line λ7789 showed a strong asymmetry which remained *constant* over the solar disk, in total disagreement with calculations based on his three-stream model. He attributed this result to the presence of an unknown blend.

A second way in which the inhomogeneity of the photosphere can influence a Fraunhofer line is by causing a *displacement*, an effect related to the asymmetry discussed above. Precise measurement of the absolute wavelengths of Fraunhofer lines is a problem fraught with technical difficulties. Nevertheless, M. G. Adam at Oxford has been able to demonstrate that the observed wavelengths fail to show the correct value of the gravitational red-shift predicted by relativity theory, the magnitude of the discrepancy varying from centre to limb. Schröter [1957] attributed this discrepancy to the Doppler velocities of the granules and succeeded in deriving a two-stream

TABLE 4.4—*Utrecht Reference Model of the Photosphere and Low Chromosphere* [*Heintze et al.*, 1964]

z (km)	p (dynes/cm²)	τ_{av}	τ_h	τ_c	T_{av} (°K)	T_h (°K)	T_c (°K)	$(p_e)_{av}$ (dynes/cm²)	$(p_e)_h$ (dynes/cm²)	$(p_e)_c$ (dynes/cm²)
635	6.17×10^2	0.00010	—	—	5125	—	—	1.41×10^{-1}	—	—
592	8.91	0.00015	—	—	5070	—	—	1.51	—	—
558	1.15×10^3	0.00020	—	—	5015	—	—	1.67	—	—
517	1.61	0.00030	—	—	4970	—	—	1.85	—	—
479	2.23	0.00045	—	—	4910	—	—	2.08	—	—
440	3.10	0.00070	—	—	4845	—	—	2.38	—	—
409	3.99	0.0010	—	—	4795	—	—	2.66	—	—
374	5.26	0.0015	—	—	4740	—	—	3.05	—	—
350	6.32	0.0020	—	—	4700	—	—	3.40	—	—
318	8.24	0.0030	—	—	4645	—	—	3.97	—	—
288	1.06×10^4	0.0045	—	—	4600	—	—	4.68	—	—
260	1.51	0.0070	—	—	4550	—	—	5.62	—	—
239	1.71	0.010	—	—	4530	—	—	6.52	—	—
219	2.18	0.015	—	—	4505	—	—	7.73	—	—
197	2.57	0.020	—	—	4500	—	—	8.93	—	—
173	3.26	0.030	—	—	4590	—	—	1.18×10^0	—	—
150	4.14	0.045	—	—	4730	—	—	1.62	—	—
124	5.30	0.070	—	—	4920	—	—	2.38	—	—
104.5	6.46	0.10	0.100	0.100	5100	5104	5096	3.37	3.52×10^0	3.47×10^0
81.8	7.98	0.15	0.153	0.153	5310	5351	5266	5.32	5.45	5.12
66.8	9.12	0.20	0.204	0.202	5480	5546	5410	7.67	8.38	6.87
46.0	1.10×10^5	0.30	0.315	0.300	5735	5845	5620	1.33×10^1	1.66×10^1	1.06×10^1
27.5	1.27	0.45	0.502	0.436	5990	6152	5814	2.41	3.30	1.70
10.8	1.47	0.70	0.853	0.633	6320	6578	6026	4.79	8.18	2.81
0	1.58	1.0	1.283	0.824	6630	6974	6234	9.57	1.76×10^2	4.37
−11.0	1.71	1.5	2.057	1.119	6980	7412	6479	1.81×10^2	3.74	7.53
−19.0	1.79	2.0	2.937	1.418	7220	7706	6648	2.70	6.04	1.04×10^2
−30.0	1.91	3.0	4.83	2.006	7585	8121	6943	5.09	1.10×10^3	1.82
−40.1	2.01	4.5	7.58	2.837	7940	8503	7268	8.97	1.85	3.24
−50.4	2.15	7.0	11.09	4.16	8285	8869	7597	1.48×10^3	2.99	5.66
−58.1	2.27	10.0	15.93	5.61	8550	9142	7857	2.04	4.09	8.49

Note: the subscripts 'av', 'h', 'c' indicate average, hot, and cold elements respectively; z is measured upwards, zero level corresponding to unit optical depth; p_e is the electron pressure. Strictly speaking, the gas pressure p applies only to the average model; however, with only small error it can also be applied to the hot and cold models. The optical depths τ refer to a wavelength of 5000Å.

photospheric model consistent with the observations. According to Schröter's model (see his Table 2), the temperature difference between the hot and cold elements (measured at equal optical depths) is ~ 800°K at $\tau_{5010} = 1$.

As an example of an inhomogeneous model, Table 4.4 gives a three-stream model of the photosphere and a homogeneous model of the low chromosphere that the Utrecht workers [Heintze, Hubenet, and de Jager, 1964] have recently proposed as a useful working model. The Utrecht workers are careful not to invest their model with any spurious respectability: their aim is rather to suggest an 'agreed' model to which future theoretical and observational investigations at Utrecht can conveniently be referred. For this reason they call their model the 'Utrecht reference photosphere 1964'.

The model given in Table 4.4 is, for the 'average' element, in broad agreement with the homogeneous model already presented in Table 4.3 (Section 4.3.2). The variation with depth of the temperature difference between the hot and cold elements is partly based on Voigt's [1956] results; in addition, the model reproduces Rösch's [1962] observed value of the granular contrast, namely

$$\frac{I_{max}-I_{min}}{\frac{1}{2}(I_{max}+I_{min})} = 21 \text{ per cent.}$$

For a more detailed discussion of the basis of the Utrecht model, the reader should consult the original paper.

In conclusion it should be pointed out that much potential information is lost by using, in effect, an averaged profile, as was done by Voigt and Schröter. Ideally, observations should be obtained of sufficient spatial resolution to separate the 'hot' and 'cold' profiles. The recent success achieved by Evans and his collaborators (see Plate 2.4) shows that even with existing techniques this is no longer impossible. Such observations would enable inhomogeneous models derived from future high-quality observations of the granular contrast to be reliably extended to the upper levels of the photosphere where the Fraunhofer lines are formed.

4.6.3 NON-UNIFORM RADIATIVE TRANSFER THEORY

Conventional radiative transfer theory [see, for example, Chandrasekhar, 1950] normally assumes the absence of horizontal variations in such quantities as the source function, the attenuation coefficient, and the total intensity, any variation being confined to the z-direction. While this approach has been successfully applied to a vast range of problems in astrophysics and solar physics, it is inadequate for exact discussions of the radiative properties of the granulation including, for example, the granular contrast and its centre-limb variation.

However, in recent years several authors, notably P. R. Wilson of the University of Sydney, have adopted a non-uniform approach from the outset. To date, Wilson's work has necessarily been of an exploratory nature, owing to the inadequacy of the observational data. Nevertheless, it seems appropriate to describe briefly the basis of his approach since the years to come will undoubtedly see an increasing interest in the application of such methods to the interpretation of the granulation and other small-scale solar structures.

The basic equation of non-uniform radiative transfer used by Wilson was originally derived by R. G. Giovanelli, using an approximation similar to the well-known Eddington approximation. It may be stated in the form

$$\nabla^2 J = \frac{1}{\kappa}\,\mathrm{grad}\,J \cdot \mathrm{grad}\,\kappa + 3\kappa^2 (J - 4\pi S), \tag{4.38}$$

where $J = \int_{4\pi} I \, d\omega$ is the total intensity, S is the source function, and κ is the attenuation coefficient ($= \rho \times$ mass absorption coefficient). In the most general case, J, S, and κ are functions of all three co-ordinates x, y, and z.

For an atmosphere in radiative equilibrium, $S = J/4\pi$, whereas for an atmosphere in convective equilibrium,

$$S = \frac{J}{4\pi} + \frac{\varepsilon}{\kappa}, \tag{4.39}$$

where ε represents the energy emitted per second per unit volume and solid angle due to the liberation of convective energy [Wilson, 1962]. Equation (4.38) then becomes

$$\mathrm{div}\left(\frac{1}{\kappa}\,\mathrm{grad}\,J\right) = -12\pi\varepsilon. \tag{4.40}$$

In the paper cited above, the various quantities were taken to be functions of *two co-ordinates only*, namely x and z. The method of solving (4.40) was to assume plausible mathematical expressions for $J(x,z)$ and $\varepsilon(x,z)$ and then to solve for $\kappa(x,z)$. Some of the various parameters in the expressions for J and ε could then be evaluated by comparing the *mean* value of $\kappa(x,z)$ (i.e. averaged horizontally) with the corresponding values of the attenuation coefficient derived by conventional radiative transfer theory; for this comparison Wilson used Plaskett's [1955] model photosphere, which is derived from limb darkening data.

For $J(x,z)$ and $\varepsilon(x,z)$ Wilson chose the expressions

$$J(x, z) = Ae^{qz} + B + Ce^{-rz} \cos Kx \tag{4.41}$$

and

$$\varepsilon(x, z) = \varepsilon_0 z e^{-sz} (1 + D \cos Kx), \tag{4.42}$$

where $z \geqslant 0$. At the surface ($z = 0$) equation (4.41) gives a sinusoidal variation for J; the quantity $2\pi/K$ is identified with the mean distance between the centres of adjacent granules, so that the parameter K has the same meaning as in previous sections of this chapter. Below the surface the mean value of J increases exponentially, while the amplitude of the horizontal variation of J decreases exponentially. The mean value of ε increases to a maximum at a certain distance below the surface and then declines to zero.

The horizontally-averaged values of J, ε, and κ must, of course, be fitted to known data. This provides a means of determining some of the parameters in (4.41) and (4.42). However, the parameters C, r, and D describing the horizontal variations in J and ε can be obtained only if the granular contrast as a function of heliocentric angle is known. In the absence of this data, the analysis has to stop at this point.[14]

In a later paper, Wilson [1964] varied his method of solution by assuming an expression for the *source function* $S(x,z)$ instead of expressions for $J(x,z)$ and $\varepsilon(x,z)$. Moreover, $\kappa(x,z)$ was calculated from the assumed model for S (using the method of model atmospheres), while $\varepsilon(x,z)$ was derived from the equation

$$\operatorname{div}\left[\frac{1}{\kappa}\operatorname{grad}\left(S-\frac{\varepsilon}{\kappa}\right)\right] = -3\varepsilon, \tag{4.43}$$

which is obtained by eliminating J between (4.39) and (4.40). The source function was assumed to be of the form

$$S(x,z) = S_0(z) + (A+Bz)\,e^{-rz}\cos Kx, \tag{4.44}$$

the second term of which increases to a maximum at a point $z = 1/r - A/B$ below the surface and thereafter tends to zero. As before, $2\pi/K$ is identified with the mean cell size of the granulation.

In the absence of reliable data on the centre-limb variation of the granular contrast, Wilson [1963b, 1964] has applied his analysis to the interpretation of Edmonds' [1962] measurements of the magnitude of the *r.m.s. brightness fluctuation* as a function of heliocentric angle (cf. Section 2.2.6). However, these attempts have met with only partial success.

To conclude this section, we must emphasize once again that the derivation of inhomogeneous photospheric models can make little real progress until reliable measurements of the granular contrast and its variation with heliocentric angle are available. Moreover, in future discussions based on non-uniform radiative transfer theory, it would be highly desirable to extend the analysis to the three-dimensional case. Finally, some attempt should be made to select representations of the various quantities more realistic than those given by (4.41), (4.42), and (4.44): for example, the sinusoidal terms in these expressions may well be inappropriate, since we know that the dark spaces between the granules are much narrower than the granules themselves (see Section 2.2.5).

[14] Wilson [1963a] subsequently obtained a formal solution for $\kappa(x,y,z)$ in terms of J and ε for the *three-dimensional* case. However, he did not attempt to apply the results to the granulation.

REFERENCES

ALLER, L. H. [1963] *Astrophysics – The Atmospheres of the Sun and Stars*. (Ronald Press: New York).

BATCHELOR, G. K. [1953] *The Theory of Homogeneous Turbulence*. (Cambridge Univ. Press).

BÖHM, K. H. [1954a] 'Die Temperaturschichtung der Sonnenatmosphäre im nichtgrauen Strahlungsgleichgewicht', *Z. Astrophys.* **34,** 182.

BÖHM, K. H. [1954b] 'Zur Deutung der Mitte-Rand-Variation der Fraunhofer-Linien', *Z. Astrophys.* **35,** 179.

BÖHM, K. H. [1958] 'Über die Grösse der Konvektionselemente in Schichten mit variablem Temperaturgradienten', *Z. Astrophys.* **46,** 245.

BÖHM, K. H. [1963a] 'Unstable modes in the solar hydrogen convection zone', *Astrophys. J.* **137,** 881.

BÖHM, K. H. [1963b] 'Strömungsformen verschiedener vertikaler Wellenlängen in der solaren Wasserstoffkonvektionszone', *Z. Astrophys.* **57,** 265.

BÖHM, K. H., and RICHTER, E. [1959] 'Der Einfluss des Strahlungsaustauches auf die Konvektion in einer polytropen Atmosphäre', *Z. Astrophys.* **48,** 231.

BÖHM, K. H., and RICHTER, E. [1960] 'Konvektion in einer Atmosphäre mit tiefenabhängigem Temperaturgradienten und starker Dichtevariation', *Z. Astrophys.* **50,** 79.

BÖHM-VITENSE, E. [1958] 'Über die Wasserstoffkonvektionszone in Sternen verschiedener Effektivtemperaturen und Leuchtkräfte', *Z. Astrophys.* **46,** 108.

CHANDRASEKHAR, S. [1950] *Radiative Transfer*. (Clarendon Press: Oxford).

CHANDRASEKHAR, S. [1953] 'The instability of a layer of fluid heated below and subject to Coriolis forces', *Proc. Roy. Soc.* A **217,** 306.

CHANDRASEKHAR, S. [1961] *Hydrodynamic and Hydromagnetic Stability*. (Oxford Univ. Press).

CHANDRASEKHAR, S., and ELBERT, D. D. [1955] 'The instability of a layer of fluid heated below and subject to Coriolis forces. II', *Proc. Roy. Soc.* A **231,** 198.

EDMONDS, F. N. [1957] 'The coefficients of viscosity and thermal conductivity in the hydrogen convection zone', *Astrophys. J.* **125,** 535.

EDMONDS, F. N. [1962] 'A statistical photometric analysis of granulation across the solar disk', *Astrophys. J. Suppl.* **6,** 357.

GILLE, J., and GOODY, R. [1964] 'Convection in a radiating gas', *J. Fluid Mech.* **20,** 47.

HEINTZE, J. R. W., HUBENET, H., and JAGER, C. DE [1964] 'A reference model of the solar photosphere and low chromosphere', *Bull. Astron. Inst. Neth.* **17,** 442.

HULST, H. C. VAN DE [1953] 'The chromosphere and the corona'. (*The Sun*, ed. G. KUIPER, p. 207; Univ. Chicago Press).

JAGER, C. DE [1959] 'Structure and dynamics of the solar atmosphere'. (*Handbuch der Physik*, ed. S. FLÜGGE, vol. 52, p. 80; Springer: Berlin).

KATO, S. [1961] 'The effect of the variation of the superadiabatic temperature gradient on the convective motion', *Publ. Astron. Soc. Japan* **13**, 410.

KHOSLA, P. K., and MURGAI, M. P. [1963] 'A study of the combined effect of thermal radiative transfer and rotation on the gravitational stability of a hot fluid', *J. Fluid Mech.* **16**, 97.

KUO, H. L. [1954] 'Symmetrical disturbances in a thin layer of fluid subject to a horizontal temperature gradient and rotation', *J. Met.* **11**, 399.

KUO, H. L. [1961] 'Solution of the non-linear equations of cellular convection and heat transport', *J. Fluid Mech.* **10**, 611.

KUPERUS, M. [1965] 'The transfer of mechanical energy in the Sun and the heating of the corona', *Rech. Astron. Utrecht* **17**, No. 1.

KUZNETSOVA, T. D., and FRANK-KAMENETSKII, D. A. [1962] 'Radiative thermal conductivity of a fully ionized plasma', *Astron. J. U.S.S.R.* **39**, 247 (*Sov. Astron. AJ* **6**, 191).

LEDOUX, P., SCHWARZSCHILD, M., and SPIEGEL, E. A. [1961] 'On the spectrum of turbulent convection', *Astrophys. J.* **133**, 184.

LEDOUX, P., and WALRAVEN, T. [1958] 'Variable stars'. (*Handbuch der Physik*, ed. S. FLÜGGE, vol. 51, p. 353; Springer: Berlin).

LEIGHTON, R. B. [1963] 'The solar granulation', *Ann. Rev. Astron. Astrophys.* **1**, 19.

MALKUS, W. V. R. [1954] 'Discrete transitions in turbulent convection', *Proc. Roy. Soc.* A **225**, 185.

MALKUS, W. V. R. [1960] 'Convection and granulation: Discussion'. (*Aerodynamic Phenomena in Stellar Atmospheres*, ed. R. N. THOMAS, p. 349; I.A.U. Symposium No. 12: *Nuov. Cim. Suppl.* **22**, No. 1).

MALKUS, W. V. R., and VERONIS, G. [1958] 'Finite amplitude cellular convection', *J. Fluid Mech.* **4**, 225.

NAKAGAWA, Y., and PRENDERGAST, K. H. [1958] 'Experimental work at the University of Chicago on the onset of thermal instability in a layer of fluid heated from below'. (*Electromagnetic Phenomena in Cosmical Physics*, ed. B. LEHNERT, p. 61; Cambridge Univ. Press).

NIELD, D. A. [1964] 'Surface tension and buoyancy effects in cellular convection', *J. Fluid Mech.* **19**, 341.

PAGEL, B. E. J. [1964] 'The structure of the solar chromosphere', *Ann. Rev. Astron. Astrophys.* **2**, 267.

PALM, E. [1960] 'On the tendency towards hexagonal cells in steady convection', *J. Fluid Mech.* **8**, 183.

PALM, E., and ØIANN, H. [1964] 'Contribution to the theory of cellular thermal convection', *J. Fluid Mech.* **19**, 353.

PECKER, J. C. [1959] 'La zone convective des étoiles: rapport introductif'. (9th Coll. Internat. d'Astrophys., Liège. *Mém. Soc. Roy. Sci. de Liège:* Series 5, **3**, 343).

PELLEW, A., and SOUTHWELL, R. V. [1940] 'On maintained convective motion in a fluid heated from below', *Proc. Roy. Soc.* A **176,** 312.

PLASKETT, H. H. [1936] 'Solar granulation', *Mon. Not. R.A.S.* **96,** 402.

PLASKETT, H. H. [1955] 'Physical conditions in the solar photosphere'. (*Vistas in Astronomy*, ed. A. BEER, vol. 1, p. 637; Pergamon: London).

PLASKETT, H. H. [1963] 'Heat flow in stars', *Observatory* **83,** 236.

PRIESTLEY, C. H. B. [1959] *Turbulent Transfer in the Lower Atmosphere.* (Univ. Chicago Press).

RAYLEIGH, LORD [1916] 'On convection currents in a horizontal layer of fluid when the higher temperature is on the under side', *Phil. Mag.* Series 6, **32,** 529.

RÖSCH, J. [1962] 'Results drawn from photographs of the photosphere obtained from the ground', *Trans. I.A.U.* **11B,** 197.

SALTZMAN, B. (ed.) [1962] *Selected Papers on the Theory of Thermal Convection.* (Dover Publications: New York).

SCHMIDT, R. J., and SAUNDERS, O. A. [1938] 'On the motion of a fluid heated from below', *Proc. Roy. Soc.* A **165,** 216.

SCHRÖTER, E. H. [1957] 'Zur Deutung der Rotverschiebung und der Mitte-Rand-Variation der Fraunhoferlinien bei Berücksichtigung der Temperaturschwankungen der Sonnenatmosphäre', *Z. Astrophys.* **41,** 141.

SCHWARZSCHILD, K. [1906] 'Über das Gleichgewicht der Sonnenatmosphäre', *Göttingen Nachr.* **1906,** 41.

SCHWARZSCHILD, M. [1959] 'Photographs of the solar granulation taken from the stratosphere', *Astrophys. J.* **130,** 345.

SCRIVEN, L. E., and STERNLING, C. V. [1964] 'On cellular convection driven by surface-tension gradients: effects of mean surface tension and surface viscosity', *J. Fluid Mech.* **19,** 321.

SEGEL, L. A., and STUART, J. T. [1962] 'On the question of the preferred mode in cellular thermal convection', *J. Fluid Mech.* **13,** 289.

SIMON, G. W., and LEIGHTON, R. B. [1964] 'Velocity fields in the solar atmosphere. III. Large-scale motions, the chromospheric network, and magnetic fields', *Astrophys. J.* **140,** 1120.

SKUMANICH, A. [1955] 'On thermal convection in a polytropic atmosphere', *Astrophys. J.* **121,** 408.

SOUFFRIN, P. [1963] 'Remarques sur les mouvements transitoires des systèmes instables. Application à un modèle de granulation solaire', *Ann. Astrophys.* **26,** 170.

SPIEGEL, E. A. [1963] 'A generalization of the mixing-length theory of turbulent convection', *Astrophys. J.* **138,** 216.

SPIEGEL, E. A. [1964a] 'The effect of radiative transfer on convective growth rates', *Astrophys. J.* **139,** 959.

SPIEGEL, E. A. [1964b] 'The solar hydrogen convection zone and its direct influence on the photosphere', *Trans. I.A.U.* **12B,** 539.

STEPANOV, V. E. [1949] 'On the problem of the electromagnetic nature of sunspots', *Sci. Trans. Lvov State Univ.: Series Phys.-Math.* **15,** 45.

STUART, J. T. [1964] 'On the cellular patterns in thermal convection', *J. Fluid Mech.* **18,** 481.

UNNO, W., KATO, S., and MAKITA, M. [1960] 'Convective instability in polytropic atmospheres. I', *Publ. Astron. Soc. Japan* **12,** 192.

UNSÖLD, A. [1955] *Physik der Sternatmosphären.* (Springer: Berlin).

VERONIS, G. [1963] 'Penetrative convection', *Astrophys. J.* **137,** 641.

VITENSE, E. [1953] 'Die Wasserstoffkonvektionszone der Sonne', *Z. Astrophys.* **32,** 135.

VOIGT, H. H. [1956] '"Drei-Strom-Modell" der Sonnenphotosphäre und Asymmetrie der Linien des infraroten Sauerstoff-Tripletts', *Z. Astrophys.* **40,** 157.

VOIGT, H. H. [1959] '"Drei-Strom-Modell" der Sonnenphotosphäre. II. Die infraroten Nickellinien $\lambda\lambda$7789 and 7798Å', *Z. Astrophys.* **47,** 144.

WASIUTYNSKI, J. [1946] 'Studies in hydrodynamics and structure of stars and planets', *Astrophysica Norvegica* **4,** Chapt. 4.

WEISS, N. O. [1964] 'Magnetic flux tubes and convection in the Sun', *Mon. Not. R.A.S.* **128,** 225.

WILSON, P. R. [1962] 'The application of the equation of transfer to the interpretation of solar granulation', *Mon. Not. R.A.S.* **123,** 287.

WILSON, P. R. [1963a] 'Three-dimensional solutions of the transfer equation', *Mon. Not. R.A.S.* **126,** 393.

WILSON, P. R. [1963b] 'An interpretation of Edmonds' granulation data', *Astrophys. J.* **137,** 606.

WILSON, P. R. [1964] 'Photospheric structure and r.m.s. fluctuation data', *Astrophys. J.* **140,** 1148.

CHAPTER 5

Current Developments in High-Resolution Observing Methods

5.1 Introduction

The previous chapter has shown that considerable progress in elucidating the physical nature of the photospheric granulation can be made on the basis of modern hydrodynamic theories of fluid convection. On the other hand, there are still serious deficiencies in present-day theories of solar convection, foremost among which is the absence of an adequate treatment taking proper account of non-linear interactions (cf. Sections 4.2.2 and 4.4.2). In this regard it is hardly necessary to emphasize that improved observations of certain crucial aspects of the photospheric granulation are likely to play a vital rôle in guiding the future development of the theory. For example, an exact knowledge of the mode of evolution of the granules and how it varies, e.g. with granule size, may be expected to throw some light on the physics of the non-linear interactions believed to occur. The following list – by no means exhaustive – gives some idea of the improvements in our observational knowledge that further development of the theory of solar convection urgently requires:

(1) a reliable determination of the granular contrast and its centre-limb variation. This is essential for the derivation of an inhomogeneous photospheric model, i.e. one that gives expression to horizontal as well as vertical variations in temperature, pressure, density, absorption coefficient, etc. (Section 4.6.3);

(2) a more precise determination of how close to the limb the granulation can still be perceived. This allows a lower limit to be placed on the height to which the convective motions penetrate into the stable layers of the photosphere, where many of the Fraunhofer lines are formed (Section 4.5.2);

(3) improved observations of the evolution of the granules (see above), including an accurate description of their modes of birth and decay (Section 2.2.8);

(4) construction of isophotal contour maps of individual granules (Section 4.4.2);

(5) determination of the actual velocity streamlines within individual granules (Section 4.4.2);

(6) improved time sequences of granulation spectra, particularly in the weaker lines, with a spatial resolution high enough to establish the precise relationship between the velocity elements and the individual granules (Section 2.4);

(7) improved observations of the correlation between the evolutionary stages passed through by a given granule and the development of a corresponding velocity oscillation (Section 2.4.3);

(8) observations of Fraunhofer line profiles with sufficient spatial resolution to separate the granules from the dark intergranular material (Section 4.6.2).

Some of the observations listed above would be feasible with only relatively minor improvements in existing techniques; others evidently would require the use of large telescopes operating outside the Earth's atmosphere. In this chapter we shall discuss current developments in high-resolution observing methods, both terrestrial and extra-terrestrial, which, it is hoped, will eventually bring such observations within the realm of possibility.

The question of solar seeing is, of course, fundamental to the whole problem of obtaining high-resolution observations from ground-based telescopes. Accordingly, we begin with a brief description of methods of measuring seeing and its basic statistical properties (Section 5.2.1), including the all-important 'intermittency effect'. In Section 5.2.2 we discuss the origin of solar seeing, basing our account on modern knowledge both of the properties of solar seeing and of the meteorological conditions prevailing in the atmospheric boundary layer. The new insight into solar seeing provided by all this recent work has important implications for the mounting and location of high-resolution telescopes; these implications are discussed in Section 5.2.3.

Proper design of the telescope is also essential to success, and in Section 5.3 we describe two modern solar telescopes specifically intended for high-resolution observations, the 12-inch refractor of the Commonwealth Scientific and Industrial Research Organization (Section 5.3.2) and the 14-inch refractor of the Fraunhofer Institut's observatory on the island of Capri (Section 5.3.3). Both telescopes use enlarging lens systems, thus providing relatively large solar images without the long optical paths usually associated with tower-type instruments; moreover, both telescopes dispense with the conventional dome. In fact, both designs set out to solve the same problems of thermal control, wind shake, weather protection, etc., although the solutions adopted are radically different. Our discussion of ground-based techniques ends with a description of an exceptionally compact spectrograph recently installed on the 26-foot 'equatorial spar' of the Sacramento Peak Observatory (Section 5.3.4). The motivation behind this development is the desire to combine the high spatial resolution of a large refractor (in this case a 16-inch coronagraph) with the high spectral resolution hitherto attainable only with large fixed solar spectrographs of conventional design.

In the field of extra-terrestrial observing methods, an exciting recent development is the decision of astronomers at the Fraunhofer Institut to attempt to obtain spectra of selected solar features, together with simultaneous photographs in white light and Hα, from a 12-inch balloon-borne telescope in the stratosphere. A pointing accuracy of $0''.1$ of arc will be achieved by means of a novel guider which makes use of a single granule. This ambitious undertaking, named 'Project Spectro-Stratoscope', is described in Section 5.4.2. The chapter ends with a brief discussion of the possible contribution which, during the next decade or so, satellite-borne telescopes and space probes may also make to our knowledge of the Sun's fine structure (Section 5.4.3).

5.2 Solar Seeing and its Origin

5.2.1 INTRODUCTION

It is now known that bad solar seeing is largely due to thermal convection currents in the first few hundred metres of the Earth's atmosphere, set up as a consequence of ground heating. Although the thermal fluctuations in this region of the atmosphere depend in a rather complicated way on various meteorological and topographical factors, their magnitude decreases quite rapidly with height. Consequently, one can improve the performance of a solar telescope simply by mounting it at a greater height above the ground provided, of course, that proper precautions are taken to shield the telescope and its supporting structure from the heating effect of the Sun (cf. Section 5.3.1).

In addition, at many sites the solar seeing displays a striking *intermittency* effect, whose existence provides another very effective way of improving the quality of solar observations. To exploit this effect, one may use a suitable photoelectric device to provide a continuous measure of the quality of the seeing and so enable the observations to be made during the sudden moments of comparative calm. This technique has been in routine use in Sydney as an aid to direct solar photography since 1959, when the present authors, in collaboration with D. G. Norton, designed and constructed a solar seeing monitor specifically for this purpose.[1] Moreover, although the use of the seeing-monitor technique has so far been restricted to direct photography, one may expect that in the future it will prove equally beneficial in the case of spectroscopic and other observations where, owing to much longer exposure times, the effect of seeing is even more critical.

The principle of operation of the Sydney seeing monitor is to measure photoelectrically the magnitude of the fluctuations in light intensity due to

[1] The term 'seeing monitor', first used by the authors in 1959, has now achieved general acceptance.

seeing of two narrow segments of the solar limb at opposite ends of an image diameter. The effect of any momentary guiding errors or wind shake on the seeing signal is minimized by adding the outputs of the two photocells receiving light from the two limb segments.[2] Since the monitor in effect measures the time variations in the distortion of the solar limb, it is intrinsically more sensitive to image *distortion* than to image degradation and, for this reason, gives only a partial assessment of the quality of the seeing. On the other hand, Zindel [1963] has constructed a seeing monitor which gives a direct indication of the degree of image *degradation*. It does this by measuring, in effect, the brightness differences between the individual photospheric granules and the larger of the dark spaces between them. At the present time other seeing monitors, mostly of the limb-distortion type, are reported to be under construction at a number of solar observatories throughout the world.

To date, however, the only published quantitative data on the statistics of good solar seeing are those which were obtained by the authors with their own seeing monitor at a flat site near Sydney [Loughhead and Bray, 1966]. In this investigation, chart recordings of the solar seeing were made over a two-year period, covering in all a total observing time of some 376 hr. Figure 5.1 shows the records obtained on four fairly typical occasions when, briefly, the seeing signal dropped below the level, shown by the dashed line, at which the situation becomes 'promising' from the point of view of 1–2″ of arc direct solar photography (0·8 volts). (There is a good correlation between the values of the seeing signal, expressed in terms of an arbitrary voltage scale, and the resolution shown by direct photographs of the photosphere taken at the same time.) All four examples provide striking demonstrations of the characteristic intermittency effect in the solar seeing: when a quiet period occurs the seeing signal declines with great rapidity, and afterwards increases to a more average value equally quickly.

The overall percentage of good seeing, averaged over the entire two-year period of observation, was found to be 0·63 per cent, or approximately 23 sec of good seeing for each hour of observation. However, there is a striking variation in the average percentage of good seeing according to the season, the figures for summer, autumn, winter, and spring being 0·13, 0·56, 1·00, and 0·73 per cent respectively. There is thus more than a sevenfold improvement between summer (0·13 per cent) and winter (1·00 per cent), the percentages for autumn and spring being about midway between these extremes. It should be emphasized, however, that these particular measurements were made at a height of only 2–2·5 m and the disparity between summer and winter may well be less at greater heights.

The distribution of moments of good seeing according to their duration

[2] For detailed information on the design and operation of this instrument the reader is referred to the following sources: Bray, Loughhead, and Norton [1959]; Bray and Loughhead [1961; 1964: p. 20]; Kuprevich [1964]; Loughhead and Bray [1966].

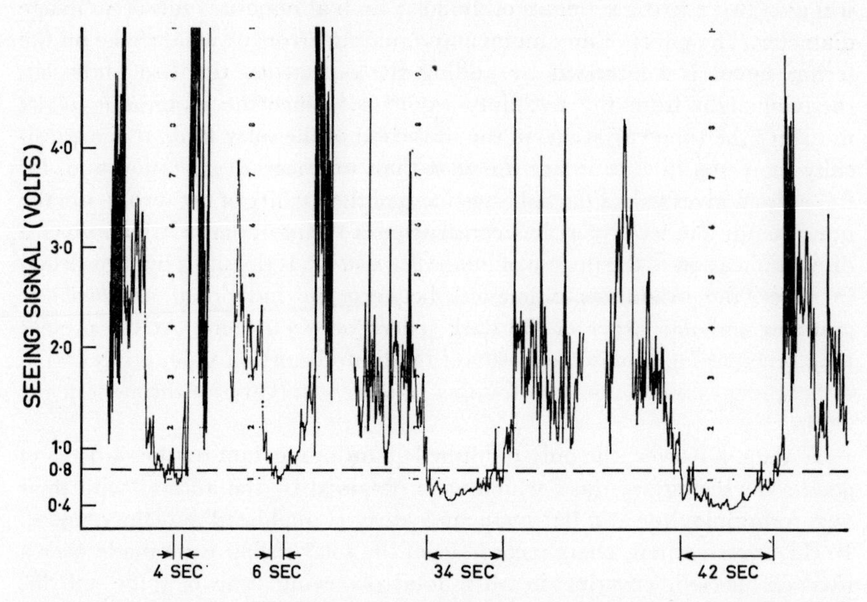

Fig. 5.1. Four fairly typical examples of moments of good seeing, demonstrating the striking suddenness of their occurrence. The dashed line indicates the 0·8 volt level at which the seeing becomes promising for high-resolution observations (see text). Most good moments are shorter than those shown, lasting no longer than 2–3 sec.

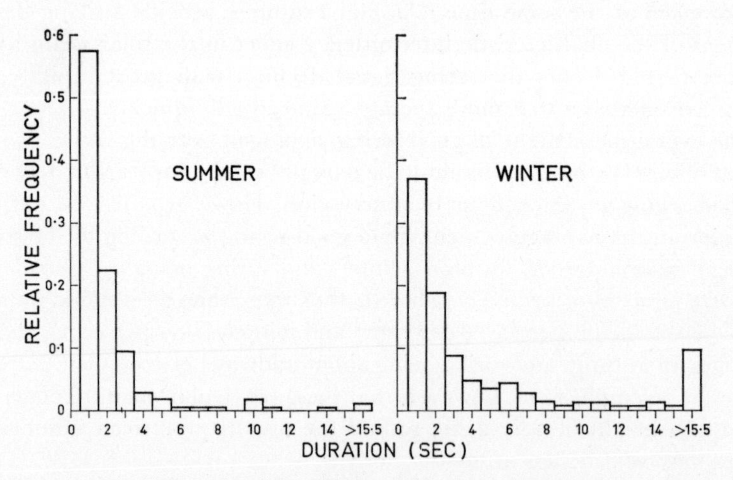

Fig. 5.2. Histograms showing the relative frequencies of moments of good seeing according to their duration, plotted separately for summer and winter. In winter the moments of good seeing are not only more frequent (6·2 per hour as opposed to 2·0 per hour in summer) but, in addition, tend to last longer. Both distributions are truncated at 0·5 sec due to the finite response time of the electronic detector circuit.

was also found to show a seasonal trend. This is illustrated by the histograms given in Fig. 5.2 for the summer and winter seasons. In both cases the frequency of good moments decreases very rapidly with increasing duration, the majority lasting for less than 1·5 sec in summer and for less than 2·5 sec in winter. However, it is evident that the actual rate of decrease is less steep in winter; in other words, in winter the moments of good seeing are not only more frequent (6·2 per hour as opposed to 2·0 per hour in summer) but, in addition, tend to last longer. Although the majority of good moments have lifetimes of less than 2–3 sec, the existence of occasional longer moments (cf. Fig. 5.2) is of great practical significance from the viewpoint of spectroscopic and other observations where exposure times of this order may be required.[3]

5.2.2 THE ORIGIN OF SOLAR SEEING

Although on occasion large-scale meteorological conditions appear to exert a dominant influence on the quality of the seeing,[4] there are nevertheless very cogent reasons for believing that under normal conditions most bad seeing originates in the boundary layer of the Earth's atmosphere in the immediate vicinity of the telescope; this extends upwards from the ground to a height of a few hundred metres. Two distinct physical factors combine to bring this about:

(1) there is abundant evidence from both daytime and night-time observations to show that thermal disturbances located *close* to a telescope are more effective in producing image distortion and degradation than those occurring further away [see, for example, Bray and Loughhead, 1964: p. 23; Siedentopf and Unz, 1964]; and

(2) during the day the short-period temperature fluctuations in the boundary layer caused by ground heating are much greater than those higher up in the atmosphere.

This is not to say that there is no contribution to bad solar seeing from the higher levels. In fact, small distortions of the limb, uncorrelated between closely neighbouring points, are presumably due to temperature inhomogeneities at greater heights than those responsible for large-scale distortions

[3] Other questions investigated included the distribution of the good moments according to time of day and the seasonal variation of this distribution. In addition, an attempt was made to discover if there is any recognizable pattern in the local meteorological conditions on days of very good seeing, on the one hand, and on days of very bad seeing, on the other. For details the reader should consult the original paper [Loughhead and Bray, 1966].

[4] For example, in Australia the arrival of a cold front from the south or south-west is always accompanied by a very marked deterioration in the seeing [Loughhead and Bray, 1966]. In the northern hemisphere the same effect has been observed by Kiepenheuer [1963: p. 216] to accompany the arrival of cold air from the north or north-east. The meteorological explanation given by Kiepenheuer is that cold masses of air are generally associated with an unstable vertical distribution of temperature, which may change drastically as the result of even small disturbances.

affecting the whole image. The reason for this is that for closely neighbouring points the image-forming rays travel through nearly identical portions of the lower atmosphere. On the other hand, any distortion on a scale greater than, say, 2′ of arc probably originates within about 150 m of the telescope, i.e. well within the atmospheric boundary layer. A seeing monitor of the limb-distortion type does not, of course, discriminate between different scales of distortion. It is, however, more sensitive to bodily displacements of large segments of the limb than to small ripples, whose effect on the monitor photocells is diminished by averaging along the length of the slits.

The first attempt to interpret the occurrence of sudden moments of good solar seeing in terms of the physical processes occurring in the atmospheric boundary layer was made by the present authors [Bray and Loughhead, 1961] on the basis of discussion with Dr C. H. B. Priestley of the C.S.I.R.O. Division of Meteorological Physics. During the past couple of decades the physical conditions in the boundary layer have been subject to much investigation, both theoretical and observational, particularly by workers in the U.S.S.R. and by Priestley and his colleagues at Melbourne. As a result, quite a detailed picture is now available of the structure of this region, a convenient summary of which has recently been published by Webb [1964].[5]

According to Webb, over flat terrain there exist three distinct regimes: a *forced* convection regime close to the ground, where the heat is carried upwards by turbulent motions generated by surface wind; a *composite* convection regime, where the motions carrying the heat are set up partly by the wind and partly by buoyancy forces; and a *free* convection regime, where buoyancy forces are dominant. The transitions between the three regimes are well-marked and occur at heights z determined by the value of the so-called Obukhov parameter

$$L = \frac{-u_*^3}{kgH/c_p\rho\theta}\,.$$

Here u_* is the 'friction velocity', k von Kármán's constant ($\simeq 0{\cdot}4$), g the acceleration due to gravity, H the vertical heat flux, c_p the specific heat of air at constant pressure, ρ the air density, and θ the mean absolute temperature.[6] It is important to note that the friction velocity u_* is roughly proportional to the horizontal wind speed U, its exact value depending on the nature and roughness of the particular terrain. As a guide to the numerical value of $|L|$, Webb quotes a typical value of around 50 m for a wind strength of 5 m/sec over grassland on a clear summer day in middle latitudes. As shown in Fig. 5.3(*a*), the transition from the forced to the composite convection region occurs at a height where $z/|L| \simeq 0{\cdot}03$, i.e. at $z \simeq 1{\cdot}5$ m under the conditions just stated. Hence the presence of the forced convection region

[5] More detailed accounts are given by Priestley [1959] and Lumley and Panofsky [1964].

[6] Strictly speaking, θ is the potential temperature, which is related to the mean actual temperature T by the formula $\partial\theta/\partial z = \partial T/\partial z + 0{\cdot}01\,^\circ\mathrm{C\ m^{-1}}$ [Webb, 1964].

may be ignored in discussing the origin of solar seeing unless the telescope is *very* close to the ground and the wind very strong.

On the other hand, the transition from the composite to the free convection region does not occur until $z/|L| \simeq 1$ (cf. Fig. 5.3(*a*)), i.e. at a typical height of 50 m if the wind speed is 5 m/sec. However, since L is roughly proportional to the cube of the wind speed, the height of the transition falls drastically to only about 3 m if the wind drops to 2 m/sec. According to the observations of Tatarskii [1956], the establishment of a new stationary convective regime consequent on a sudden change in wind speed takes place remarkably quickly, the whole process probably occupying no more than about a minute.

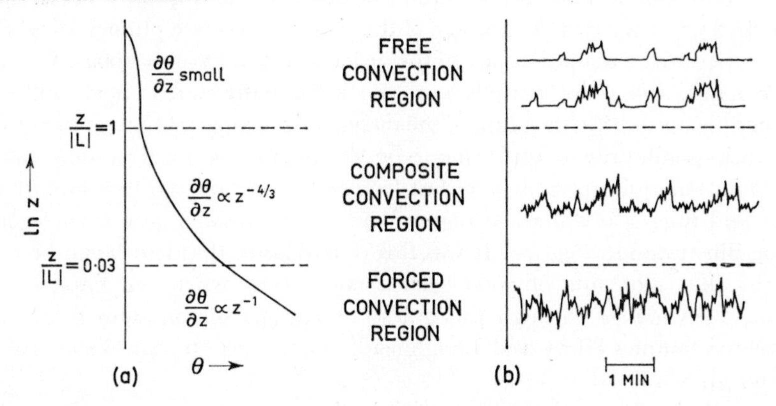

Fig. 5.3. Convection in the boundary layer of the Earth's atmosphere over flat terrain resulting from heating of the ground by the Sun [adapted from Webb, 1964].

(*a*) Stratification into regions of forced, composite, and free convection. The transition heights are determined by the value of the Obukhov parameter L, which is defined in the text. θ is the potential temperature and z is the height above ground level in metres.

(*b*) Typical measured temperature fluctuations within the three separate convection regions. The flat portions of the upper two traces are identified with moments of good seeing.

Figure 5.3(*b*) illustrates the nature of the temperature fluctuations associated with the three separate convective regions [Webb, 1964]. In the forced convection region the temperature traces have the random appearance typical of purely turbulent fluctuations. In the composite region, on the other hand, in addition to the random fluctuations[7] there are discrete periods of marked temperature enhancement ('bursts'), which become more prominent with increasing height. Throughout much of this region and in the free convection zone above it, many of the bursts are recorded almost

[7] The r.m.s. deviation σ_T of the random temperature fluctuations in the composite convection region around the mean value may be estimated from the approximate relation

$$\sigma_T \simeq 0{\cdot}15\, H^{2/3}\, z^{-1/3}$$

given by Webb [1964]; thus σ_T increases as the two-thirds power of the heat flux.

simultaneously by instruments placed at different heights, showing that they have the form of *buoyant plumes* extending upwards to a considerable height (perhaps around $10|L|$ according to Webb). However, the temperature bursts are generally registered slightly earlier at higher levels than at lower levels, indicating that the plumes are tilted as they are carried along by the wind; Webb gives a tentative assessment of the angle of tilt as 30–45°. In addition, there is generally a decrease in the duration of the recorded temperature bursts in the upper part of the free convection region, implying that the width of the plumes tends to *decrease* with height.

In the free convection region, as illustrated in Fig. 5.3(*b*), the temperature traces show a well-marked alternation of disturbed and quiet periods. The disturbed periods mark the passage of the rising convective plumes, in which the temperature fluctuations are of the order of 1–2°C [Webb, 1964]. On the other hand, the quiet periods are associated with much more uniform descending air outside the plumes, the magnitude of any residual temperature fluctuations still present appearing to be less than 0·1°C [cf. Priestley, 1959: Fig. 19]. The quiet periods may last from a few seconds up to a minute or more and thus bear a marked resemblance to the sudden moments of good seeing illustrated in Fig. 5.1. It was this resemblance that led the authors to suggest that moments of good solar seeing occur when the line-of-sight momentarily passes through the quiescent regions surrounding the rising convective plumes [Bray and Loughhead, 1961, 1964: p. 26; Webb, 1964: cf. Fig. 5].

On the other hand, the quiet periods in the temperature traces seem to be more frequent than the moments of good seeing and they also appear to last somewhat longer. These discrepancies can be understood, however, when it is realized that the telescope has to look through a forest of convective plumes: good seeing occurs only when, momentarily, a 'clear' patch lies along the line-of-sight. For geometrical reasons it is obvious that the best chance of obtaining good seeing occurs when the line-of-sight is inclined parallel to the convective plumes, i.e. when the Sun happens to be at the right zenith angle downwind from the observer. This means that, especially on days of light wind, there should generally be a tendency for good seeing to occur around noon.

On the basis of the above considerations, the best seeing will evidently occur at moments when the Obukhov parameter $|L|$ happens to be less than the height of the telescope, thus ensuring that $z/|L|$ is greater than 1. Otherwise the line-of-sight must pass through part of the region of composite convection, where marked temperature fluctuations are present even in the air outside the plumes. Moreover, as Webb [1964] has pointed out, the greater the height of the telescope compared to $|L|$, the longer in general should the good moments last.

In conclusion, we must emphasize that the systematic study of the properties of the solar seeing and of its meteorological interpretation is still in its

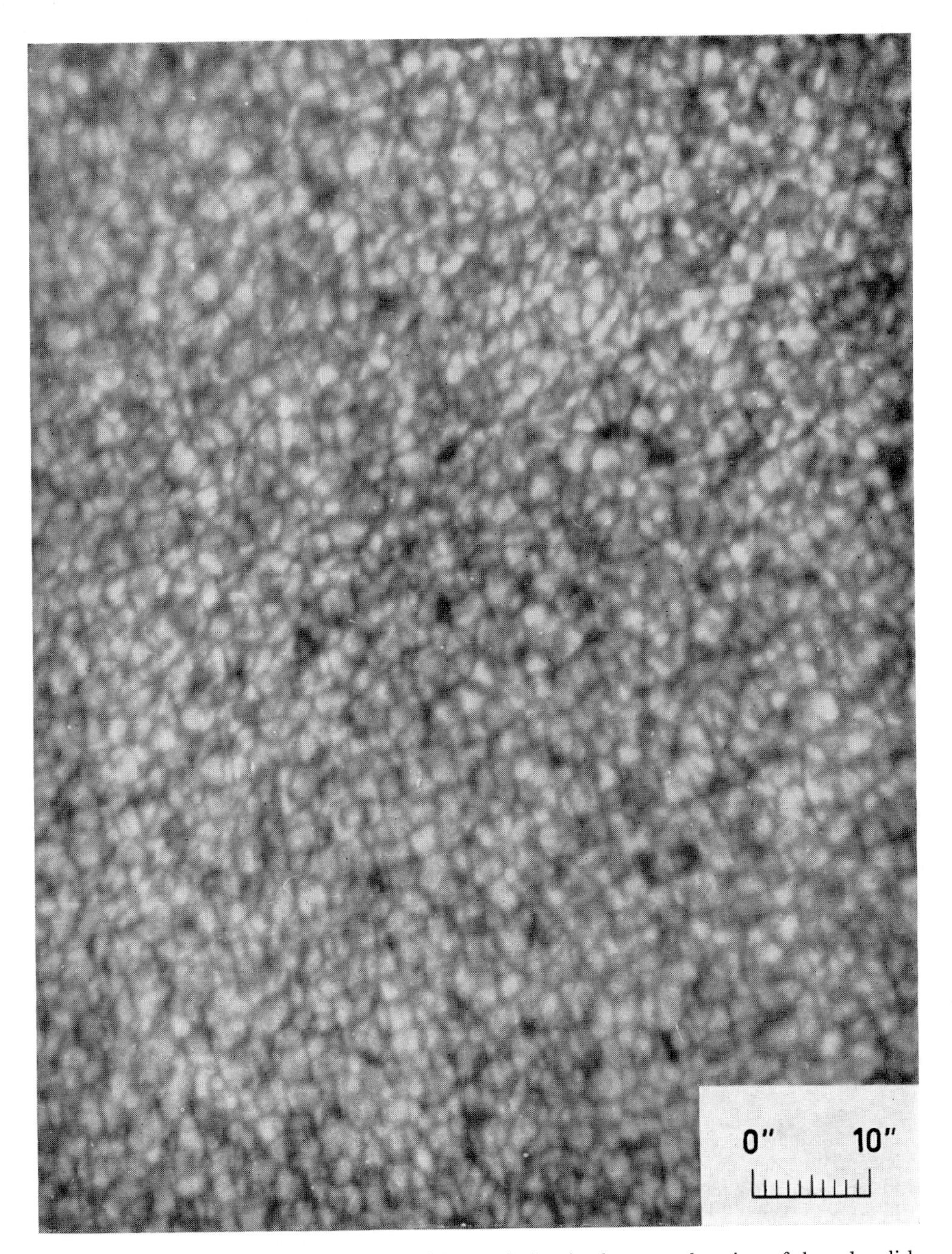

PLATE 5.1. Photograph of the photospheric granulation in the central region of the solar disk obtained by J. W. Harvey with the 150-foot Mt Wilson solar tower (objective diameter 12 inches). The resolution approaches that attained by the best stratospheric photographs (cf. Plate 2.1). (*By courtesy of Mt Wilson Observatory.*)

PLATE 5.2. The C.S.I.R.O. 12-inch solar refractor shown mounted on its tower. The tower is actually a double structure, although this is not apparent in the photograph. The inner tower carries the telescope and the outer tower carries the canopy, one side of which is here shown partially closed. When the telescope is not in use, it is turned east-west and the canopy is fully raised to cover it.

PLATE 5.3. The domeless coudé refractor of the Fraunhofer Institut seen at the Zeiss works near Oberkochen, prior to its transportation to the island of Capri. The control desk can be seen at the left. (*By courtesy of Carl Zeiss.*)

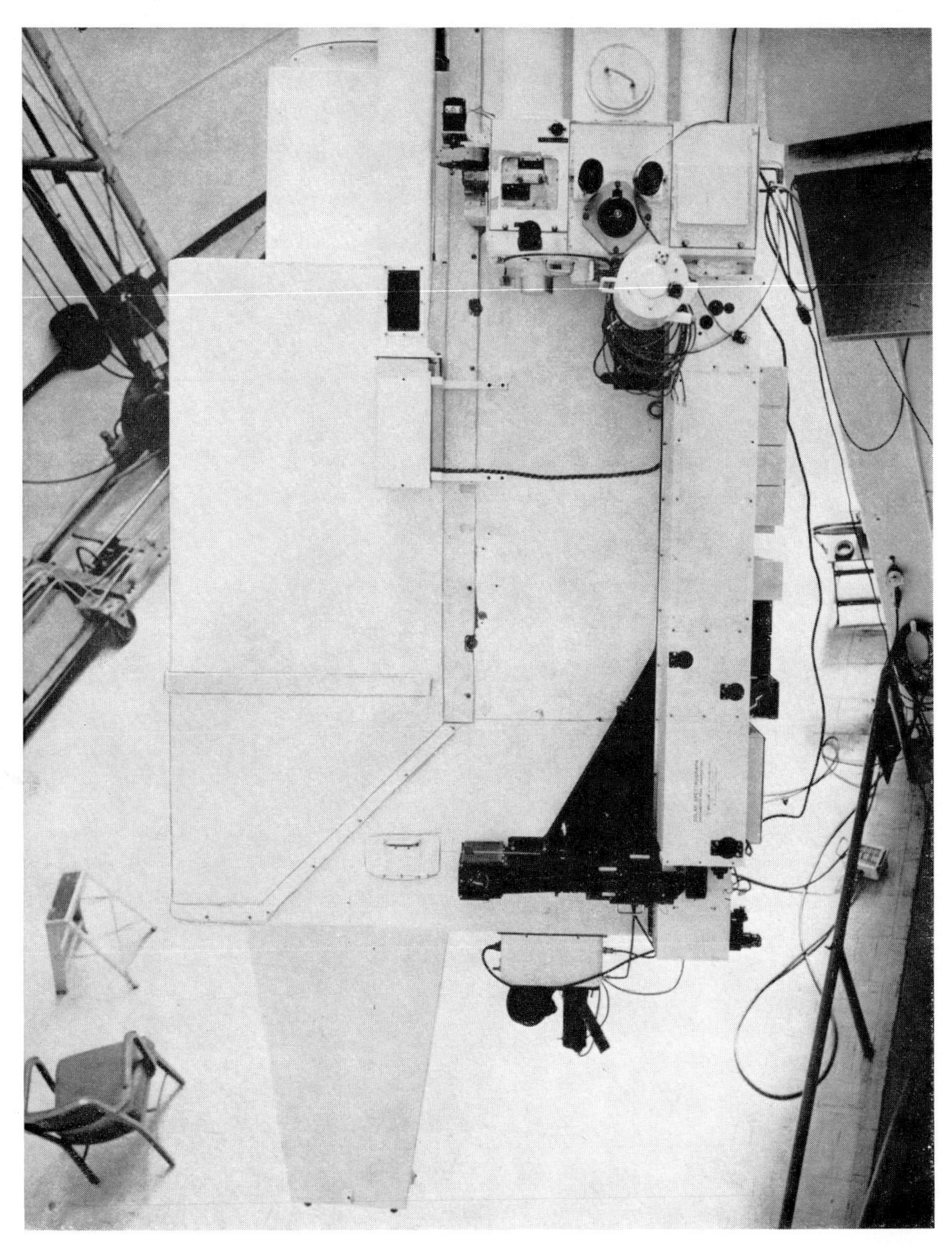

PLATE 5.4. The 12-metre compact spectrograph at Sacramento Peak. The instrument is carried on the lower end of a 26-foot 'equatorial spar' and is housed in the narrow rectangular box visible on the right; the camera is part of the dark-coloured assembly to the left of the box. The physical length of the spectrograph is only 1·8 m. (*By courtesy of Sacramento Peak Observatory.*)

infancy. More observations of the kind described in Section 5.2.1 are urgently needed, particularly at heights where the seeing monitor telescope would be situated more frequently in the free convection zone. Such observations should be made at as many different observing sites as possible and, in addition, they should be closely correlated with simultaneous micrometeorological measurements made with the aid of rapid-recording techniques.

5.2.3 IMPLICATIONS FOR FUTURE INSTRUMENTAL DEVELOPMENTS

As we have seen in the preceding sections, recent work has provided much valuable insight into the properties and origin of solar seeing. This new knowledge has, *inter alia*, some important implications for the mounting and location of future high-resolution solar telescopes:

(1) it is now clear that a knowledge of the values of the Obukhov parameter L likely to be encountered at the site selected, particularly those pertaining under the favourable conditions of light wind, is essential before any proper decision can be made as to the height at which the telescope should be mounted. On the other hand, the ultimate decision must still rest on financial considerations: at any given site there is an 'economic height' above which any further improvement in the seeing becomes too small to justify the additional expense involved;

(2) a site should be chosen where the terrain is flat, smooth, and free from obstructions for a considerable distance around the telescope – at least fifty times the telescope height in the estimation of Webb [1964] – since this ensures that the 'friction velocity' u_* and hence $|L|$ are as small as possible for any given wind speed. The adverse effect of surface roughness is very marked if the wind is at all strong. For example, according to a chart published by Webb (see his Fig. 6), the value of $|L|$ for a wind speed of 4 m/sec and a heat flux of 25 mW/cm^2 is about 5 m over snow, 15–30 m over open grassland, and 100 m or more over bushes. Under no circumstances should trees be grown in the general vicinity of the telescope;[8]

(3) Webb [1964] has shown that, although the refractive index is almost exactly proportional to the air density, a site on a high-altitude plateau would offer no significant advantage over one at sea level as far as the quality of the seeing is concerned. The reason is that a smaller density requires larger temperature fluctuations to maintain the heat flux, and so the *fluctuations* in density (and hence in refractive index) remain about the same.

The statistics of good solar seeing presented in Section 5.2.1 offer much encouragement to any observer wishing to obtain improved observations of the photospheric granulation from a ground-based installation – provided,

[8] Using rapid-response thermometers carried by a low-flying aircraft, Vul'fson [1964: p. 113] in the U.S.S.R. has made extensive measurements of the temperature fluctuations over open fields and forests at heights of 50–300 m. His results indicate that the convective motions over forests are more intense than those over fields.

of course, he is prepared to take full advantage of the modern technique of using a seeing monitor to trigger the telescope exposures at the moments of best seeing. The results show that, for a telescope mounted at a height of only a few metres at the site concerned, there are on the average 23 sec in each hour during which one has a good chance of obtaining direct photographs of the granulation with a spatial resolution of 1″ of arc. Moreover, it must be remembered that the statistics, as they stand, give an unduly pessimistic assessment of the situation, since at greater heights one can expect the moments of good seeing to be more frequent and to last longer. Furthermore, the spatial resolution attained during these intervals should be higher for telescopes mounted at greater heights. This expectation is well borne out by the fact that in recent years granulation photographs have been obtained by a number of ground-based observers showing a resolution approaching that of the best stratospheric photographs. The quality of these modern ground-based observations is well illustrated by Plates 2.2(*a*) and 5.1: the former was taken by J. Rösch with a 38-cm refractor at the Pic-du-Midi and the latter by J. W. Harvey with the 150-foot solar tower at Mt Wilson.

From the point of view of spectroscopic observations, on the other hand, the situation at first sight appears somewhat less promising: here exposure times of several seconds may be required, whereas the majority of moments of good seeing have lifetimes of less than 2–3 sec (cf. Fig. 5.2). Moreover, such moments – even if sufficiently prolonged – would not necessarily enable spectroscopic observations to be obtained with a resolution equal to that of direct photographs. This is due to the fact that even when the image is little degraded, shifts and distortions amounting to several seconds of arc may still be present: in direct photography the exposure time is small enough to 'freeze' the image motions to some extent, but this is not so for observations requiring exposure times amounting to several seconds. However, in such cases one might attempt to 'build up' the exposure over a number of periods of exceptionally good seeing by using a seeing-monitor triggering system equipped with an auxiliary integrating circuit to control the total exposure time.

As in the case of direct photography, further improvement in the spatial resolution attained in spectroscopic work would result if both the telescope and the associated spectrograph were mounted at a greater height above the ground, proper care being taken to shield the telescope and its supporting structure from the heating effect of the Sun. One way in which this might be done would be to accommodate both the spectrograph and a refracting telescope of the photoheliograph type on the same equatorial mounting (cf. Section 5.3.4), preferably carried on top of a double skeleton tower of suitable height. The basic principles and techniques necessary for the practical realization of such a scheme have, in fact, been incorporated to a varying extent in several installations which are currently being brought into operation as part of a new generation of ground-based solar telescopes. Underlying the design of these instruments there has been a much fuller appreciation than hitherto of the properties and origin of solar seeing and, in particular, of the ways in which its adverse effects may be greatly mitigated. Some of the more novel and interesting of these new instruments are described in the following section.

5.3 Ground-Based Solar Telescopes and Spectrographs of Advanced Design

5.3.1 INTRODUCTION

As we have seen in the previous section, our knowledge of the properties and origin of solar seeing is now sufficient to provide an objective basis for selecting a favourable site for a solar telescope and deciding on its optimum height. All of this insight is of little avail, however, if no attempt is made to optimize the design of the solar installation itself. The reason for this is simply that, in the absence of proper design, a large contribution to poor image quality can come from thermal currents originating from heating of the telescope and its dome. In such cases, of course, little or no advantage can be taken of the intermittency effect in the 'external' seeing (Section 5.2.1) and the image quality will be poor nearly all of the time.

Recent years have seen a growing realization among solar physicists that the design of a solar telescope is as much a thermal problem as an optical problem. However, it is not our aim in the sections that follow to give a detailed account of the principles underlying the optimization of telescope design; for such an account the reader should consult the authors' earlier monograph [Bray and Loughhead, 1964: Chap. 2, especially pp. 34–47]. Instead, we shall illustrate some of the modern trends in telescope design by describing just two recent telescopes specifically intended for high-resolution observations of the Sun.

The first of these is the 12-inch refractor of the Commonwealth Scientific and Industrial Research Organization (C.S.I.R.O.), which was developed by the authors in collaboration with a number of colleagues (Section 5.3.2); the second is the 14-inch refractor of the Fraunhofer Institut's observatory on the island of Capri, designed by K. O. Kiepenheuer and the late Bernard Lyot (Section 5.3.3). Both telescopes use enlarging lens systems, thus providing relatively large solar images without the long optical paths usually associated with tower-type telescopes. Moreover, both telescopes dispense with the conventional dome. In other respects, however, the designs of the two instruments are radically different although in each case the problems to be solved, namely those of thermal control, wind shake, weather protection, etc., are the same. Great interest is therefore attached to the relative performance of the two telescopes, but it will be some time before the necessary data become available.

In addition to considering the design of these two telescopes, we shall also describe a high-performance spectrograph of extremely compact design developed by J. W. Evans for the 26-foot 'equatorial spar' at the Sacramento Peak Observatory (Section 5.3.4). The motivation behind this development is the desire to combine the high spatial resolution of which a large refractor is potentially capable with the high spectral resolution hitherto attainable only with large fixed spectrographs of conventional design. A similar idea has occurred to a number of other workers [see, for example, McMath and Mohler, 1962: p. 37; Bray and Loughhead, 1964: p. 42], but the Sacramento Peak spectrograph represents its first concrete realization.

5.3.2 THE C.S.I.R.O. 12-INCH SOLAR REFRACTOR

The C.S.I.R.O. telescope is designed for high-resolution time-lapse photography of any selected region of the solar disk in either white light or Hα. Figure 5.4 shows a schematic layout of the telescope in its chromospheric mode. D_1 is a hollow aluminium shield which protects the telescope from solar heating by covering the entire front area, excluding the objective L_1 and the two auxiliary telescopes feeding a photoelectric guider and a seeing monitor. The front surface of D_1 contains numerous perforations through which air is continually drawn by a suction system. The temperature of the shield is thus kept close to the ambient value, and it performs its function of keeping the Sun's rays off other parts of the telescope without itself giving rise to damaging convection currents. The 12-inch objective lens L_1 is a high-quality air-spaced doublet of 10-foot focal length made by Grubb Parsons; tested in the laboratory, it gives excellent performance in both the red and green regions of the spectrum. L_1 forms a 28-mm solar image on a prime-focus diaphragm D_2 which, like D_1, is air-cooled. The portion of the image corresponding to the aperture in D_2 is re-imaged with the aid of two auxiliary lenses L_2 and L_3 to produce an enlarged image on the gate of a 35-mm camera C; the camera is preceded by a Lyot filter F and a reflex viewing system R.

L_3 is fixed in such a position that its focus coincides with the image of L_1 produced by L_2. This ensures that all rays coming from any given point of L_1 are parallel as they pass through the filter F, so that the 'spectral purity' is the same for all points of the final image.

Two sets of lenses L_2 and L_3 are provided, each set producing a different magnification of the primary image; the corresponding effective image diameters at the final image plane are 8·5 and 17 cm. L_2 is provided with screws giving motions in two directions at right angles to the optical axis, so that any desired region of the solar image can be brought onto the camera gate. (The optical system is designed to keep any off-axis aberrations introduced by shifting L_2 away from the optical axis of the objective within the Rayleigh limit.) A change to the alternative magnification necessitates a movement of L_2 along the optical axis; L_2 is accordingly mounted on a parallel slide. L_3, however, is mounted in a fixed position, and only the lens itself needs to be changed when the magnification is altered.

The shutter unit is mounted in front of the prime-focus diaphragm D_2 and consists of a solenoid-operated blade shutter S_1 and a rotating sector-disk shutter S_2 driven by an electric motor M. The angular opening of the sector disk can be adjusted manually in order to accommodate gross changes in the light flux.

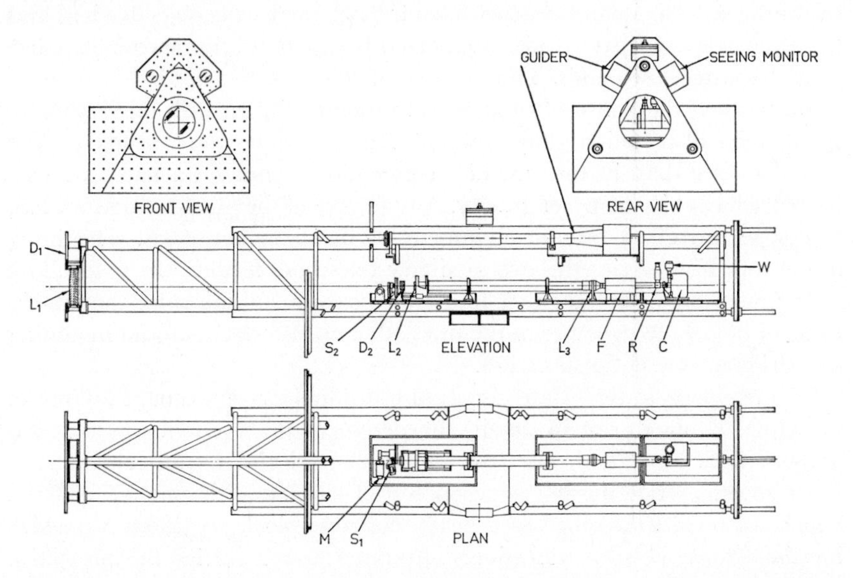

Fig. 5.4. The C.S.I.R.O. 12-inch solar refractor: optical layout. D_1, front shield; L_1, objective; D_2, prime-focus diaphragm; L_2, magnifying lens; L_3, field lens; F, Lyot filter; C, camera; R, reflex viewing system; S_1, blade shutter; S_2, sector-disk shutter; M, shutter motor. Two auxiliary 4-inch telescopes, which feed a seeing monitor and a photoelectric guider, are attached to the inner framework. The telescope mounting and tower are shown in Plate 5.2.

All operations involved in taking exposures are sequenced automatically by an electronic programme controller situated inside the control room. The triggering pulse is initiated either by the seeing monitor or, alternatively, by a timing mechanism giving pulses at intervals which can be varied from 5 to 120 sec. The image of a clock (W in Fig. 5.4), together with the date, is recorded in a corner of each frame.

The seeing monitor is fed by an auxiliary 4-inch telescope, while a second identical telescope feeds a photoelectric guider of conventional design [see, for example, Bray and Loughhead, 1964: pp. 29–30]. This telescope also feeds a photoelectric exposure controller, whose output is applied to the shutter motor M in such a way as to keep the product of the exposure time and the light flux constant. Thus exposures of uniform density are obtained regardless of varying sky transparency or solar zenith distance.

When the telescope is to be operated in the photospheric mode, the Lyot filter F and the field lens L_3 are removed. In addition, the single-disk rotating shutter S_2 at the prime focus is replaced by a double-disk high-speed shutter placed just before the camera [cf. Bray and Loughhead, 1964: p. 29].

The supporting structure for the optical and mechanical parts, i.e. the telescope 'tube', is unusual in that it consists of two open triangular frameworks, one inside the other (see Plate 5.2); both are constructed of welded steel tubing.[9] The inner framework, 20 ft long, carries the objective lens and the other telescope parts and is supported by the outer framework at points near the latter's two ends. The purpose of this arrangement is to minimize flexure: when the points of support are properly chosen with due regard to the weight distribution, any residual flexure of the inner framework is much smaller than in the case of a conventional equatorial telescope supported solely at its centre of gravity. Any flexure of the outer framework has, of course, no effect on the alignment of the telescope parts. The inner framework also carries the two auxiliary telescopes feeding the guider and seeing monitor, while the outer framework carries stub axles for the attachment of the whole structure to the tines of an open-fork equatorial mounting and drive of conventional design.

The telescope tower (Plate 5.2) is also a double structure and follows in principle, although not in detail, the design of the 150-foot tower at Mt Wilson. Both inner and outer towers are of steel girder construction. The inner tower carries the telescope on top of a reinforced concrete pedestal which, in turn, is attached to a heavy concrete block providing a massive inertia against possible vibration. The outer tower carries the protective canopy (see below) and, beneath the concrete block, the control room. The inner and outer towers are everywhere separated by a gap of approximately 2 inches, so vibration of the outer tower cannot be communicated to the telescope. In addition, light-gauge steel cladding attached to the outer tower protects the members of the inner tower from wind shake. There remains some possibility of wind vibration of the telescope itself; however, in view of the lattice-type construction of the telescope tube, this should be very small under normal weather conditions. The inner tower is supported by four concrete piles some 10 ft deep, while the outer tower is supported by eight concrete blocks each located some 4 ft from the nearest pile. The top of the telescope pedestal is nearly 50 ft above ground level, while the maximum height attained by the objective lens is approximately 65 ft.

When in use, the telescope is completely open to the air, as shown in Plate 5.2 – a very desirable feature from the thermal point of view. When not in use, the telescope is turned to the east-west direction and enclosed by a canopy, whose four motor-driven leaves rise from the sides of the supporting structure. Thermal control of the telescope's immediate environment is

[9] This design was suggested by Mr M. J. Murphy, who was also responsible for the detailed engineering design of the tower, canopy, and the equatorial mounting and drive.

aided by drawing air downwards through holes in the floor of the observing platform surrounding the pedestal.

The telescope is mounted in flat, lightly-grassed country at the C.S.I.R.O. Culgoora Solar Observatory, which is situated some 370 miles north-west of Sydney, Australia. The 96-element radio-heliograph designed by J. P. Wild is located at the same site.

5·3·3 THE DOMELESS COUDÉ REFRACTOR OF THE FRAUNHOFER INSTITUT

In 1965 a new 14-inch solar telescope, built according to a novel and highly ingenious design developed by K. O. Kiepenheuer and the late Bernard Lyot, was brought into operation at the Capri Observatory of the Fraunhofer Institut. The principal innovation is the elimination of a dome by employing two tubes and two mountings: the outer tube and mounting serves to protect the telescope from wind shake and weather, while the inner tube, which is independently mounted and guided, carries the optical parts of the telescope proper. The manufacture of the telescope was carried out by the firm of Carl Zeiss, Oberkochen, West Germany.

Figure 5.5 gives a schematic view of the instrument [Kiepenheuer, 1964]. The objective L_1 is a three-lens apochromat of aperture 35 cm (14 in) and focal length 4·45 m. D_1 is a prime-focus diaphragm performing the same function as the corresponding diaphragm in the C.S.I.R.O. telescope – namely, to prevent heat and light from all parts of the solar image except the small area under immediate observation from proceeding further into the telescope. As in the C.S.I.R.O. telescope, D_1 is cooled by air suction. Moreover, the system of fans slowly sucks air from the objective lens end of the tube downwards into the laboratory. M_1 is a coudé mirror which directs the beam to two auxiliary lenses L_2 and L_3 and a second mirror M_2. This lens system increases the image diameter from a value of 43 mm at the prime focus to 15 cm at a point in the laboratory (not marked in Fig. 5.5).

Two further auxiliary lenses L_4 and L_5 feed a spectrograph–magnetograph combination S with a 33-cm solar image. The rotation of the image resulting from the use of a coudé system is removed by a rotating Dove prism P. The autocollimating grating spectrograph has an effective focal length of 20 m, but the physical length is reduced to 10 m by means of two internal lenses L_6 and L_7. The grating G is ruled with 600 lines/mm over an area of 21×16 cm^2; blazed in the fifth order (blaze angle $= 48° 36'$), it gives a dispersion of approximately 9 mm/Å.

The photoelectric guider R makes use of portion of the main beam and operates through a servo system on the mirror M_2. However, it can be used only when the prime-focus diaphragm D_1 is removed. The guider is very quick-acting, having a time-constant of only 0·1 sec.

The telescope has no declination axis as such; however, it can be turned relative to the polar axis by rotating the upper half of the sphere carrying the telescope relative to the lower half (see Plate 5.3). The outer concrete tower is about 10 m high; this tower carries the outer shield of the telescope, while the inner tower, which is completely independent, carries the telescope proper (Fig. 5.5).

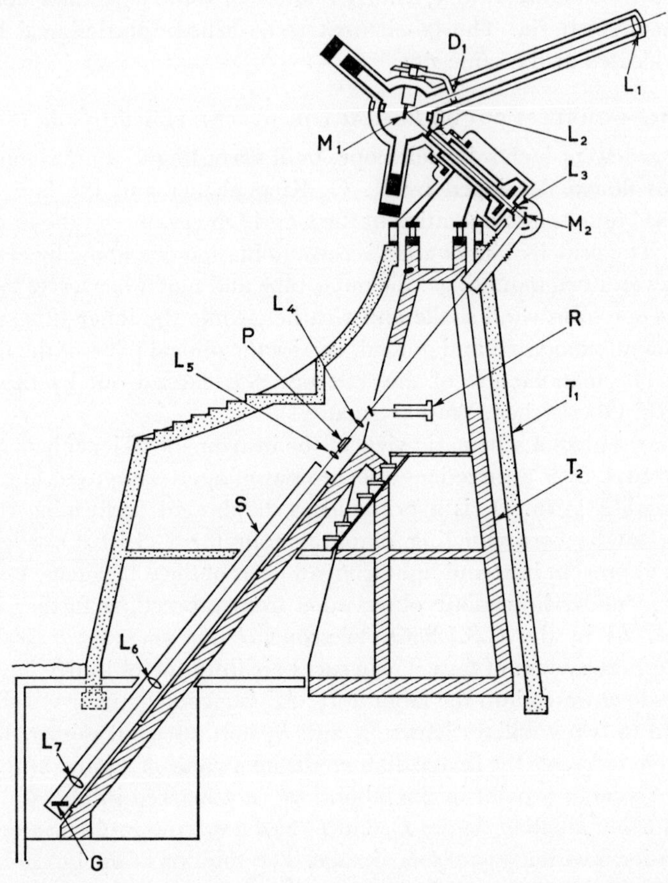

Fig. 5.5. The domeless coudé refractor of the Fraunhofer Institut: schematic layout [Kiepenheuer, 1964]. L_1, objective; D_1, prime-focus diaphragm; M_1, coudé mirror; L_2, L_3, enlarging lens system; M_2, secondary mirror; R, photoelectric guider; L_4, L_5, second enlarging lens system; P, rotating Dove prism; S, spectrograph; L_6, L_7, spectrograph lens system; G, diffraction grating. The outer concrete tower, T_1, is 10 m high and carries the outer shield of the telescope; the inner tower, T_2, carries the telescope proper. A photograph of the telescope is shown in Plate 5.3.

5.3.4 THE 12-METRE COMPACT SPECTROGRAPH AT SACRAMENTO PEAK

Plate 5.4 shows a new Littrow-type solar spectrograph of exceptionally compact design which has recently been installed at the Sacramento Peak Observatory by J. W. Evans.[10] The spectrograph receives light from a large

[10] The present section is based on information and diagrams very kindly supplied by Dr Evans.

16-inch coronagraph working at $f/15$, both instruments being accommodated on one face of a 26-foot 'equatorial spar'. The telescope is known to be capable of providing high-quality images of small-scale solar structures such as the chromospheric spicules; Evans' spectrograph is designed to provide high-dispersion spectra of such features. The physical length of the spectrograph is only 1·8 m, yet it affords an effective focal length of about 12 m. Basically, this is achieved by using a short-focus collimating mirror to form a small primary spectrum, which is then re-imaged by a magnifying lens to produce a final spectrum with a greatly increased linear dispersion.

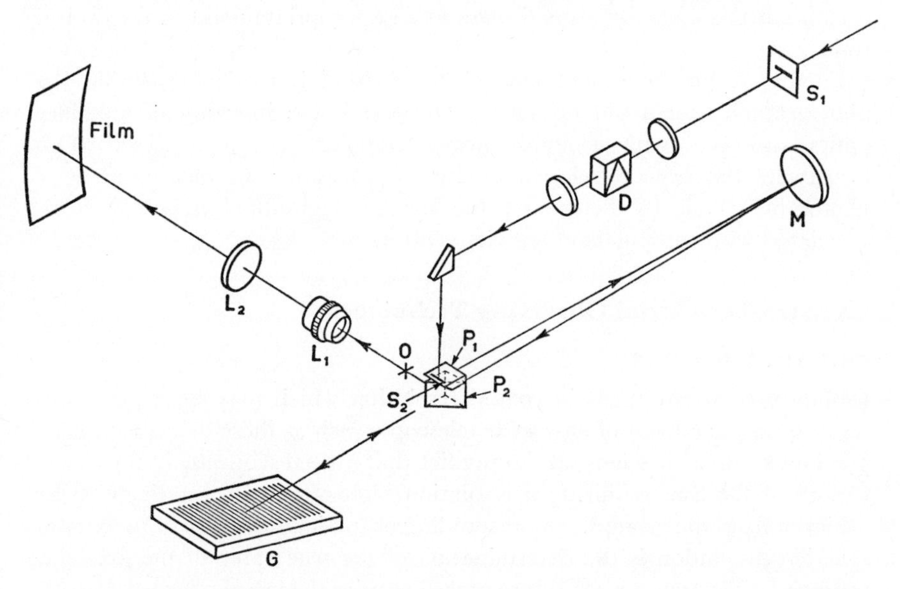

Fig. 5.6. The 12-metre compact spectrograph at Sacramento Peak: optical layout. S_1, S_2, slits; D, compound dispersing prism; P_1, P_2, prisms; M, collimating mirror; G, diffraction grating; O, position of primary spectrum; L_1, collimating lens; L_2, magnifying lens.

The optical layout of the spectrograph is shown schematically in Fig. 5.6. Light entering a slit S_1 located in the image plane of the telescope is passed through a compound dispersing prism D and is then re-focused, with some reduction in the effective image size, onto the entrance slit of the spectrograph, S_2. A prism P_1 placed immediately below S_2 diverts the light towards the collimating mirror M, which has an aperture of 18 cm and a focal length of 157 cm. After diffraction at the 10-inch grating G, the collimated beam is re-focused by M to form a small primary spectrum at a point O some 5 mm beyond a second prism P_2 placed immediately below P_1, the purpose of P_2 being to divert the light forming the spectrum into a direction at right angles to the main optical axis. The diffraction grating itself is ruled with 300 lines/mm and has a blaze angle of 64°. The light from O is collimated by a lens L_1 and is then re-imaged by a second lens L_2 to form an enlarged spectrum with a dispersion of 6–13 mm/Å and an angular scale in the direction at right angles to the dispersion of 5″.8 of arc/mm.

The final focal surface is strongly curved due to the presence of a rather powerful field lens (not shown in the diagram) on the exit face of the prism P_2, but this is satisfactorily overcome by bending the film to a cylindrical shape. In addition, a small part of the undispersed beam coming from the mirror M to the grating G goes directly into the prism P_2 and is thus a potential source of scattered light at the final focal surface; however, this is eliminated by placing a small mask at an appropriate point in the optical train.

Finally, it may be mentioned that provision is made for sliding the photographic system out of the way to permit the insertion of auxiliary optics associated with a highly novel 'Doppler–Zeeman analyser'. This instrument has been developed by Evans [1964] for the measurement of photospheric velocity fields and the strong longitudinal magnetic fields associated with sunspots and activity centres.

5.4 Extra-Terrestrial Observing Techniques

5.4.1 INTRODUCTION

Despite the improvement in spatial resolution which may be expected to result from the advent of new solar telescopes such as those described in the previous sections, it seems safe to predict that a need will remain for observations of the Sun requiring a resolution higher than is ever likely to be achieved from the ground. An outstanding example in the case of the photospheric granulation is the determination of the true value of the granular contrast (cf. Section 2.2.5): this may well require the use of a large telescope with a resolving limit of at least 0″.1 of arc (about the theoretical limit of a 50-inch objective) operating outside the atmosphere. Other examples might include the detailed mapping of the velocity field within individual granules, the determination of the exact distance from the limb at which the granulation finally disappears, the study of the detailed processes of birth and decay of individual granules, and so on.

The first step in the development of extra-terrestrial observing techniques capable of resolving such problems was made in the mid-1950's, when a number of workers in England, France, and the U.S.A. decided to build balloon-borne telescopes designed to photograph the Sun at heights above the disturbed layers of the atmosphere responsible for bad seeing (cf. Section 1.6). The culmination of these efforts was Project Stratoscope I of the Princeton University Observatory which, under the direction of M. Schwarzschild, produced photographs of the photospheric granulation of unsurpassed definition taken at heights in the vicinity of 80,000 ft. The telescope was basically a 12-inch Newtonian reflector, photoelectrically guided on the

Sun. A television link presented to the observers on the ground the same picture as that being simultaneously photographed by the telescope, and this in turn enabled its focus and orientation to be adjusted by radio command signals.[11]

The various flights of Project Stratoscope I yielded photographs of the granulation which appear to be completely devoid of seeing effects; one of the best of these photographs is shown in Plate 2.1. Moreover, although no sequences of photographs of the same region of the Sun were obtained on the early flights, the use of more refined techniques on later flights yielded sequences of granulation photographs lasting from 8 to 15 min (cf. Section 2.2.7). However, despite the valuable accomplishments of this pioneering venture, the technique of stratospheric solar photography was not fully perfected. A serious deficiency was the failure to fully solve the problem of guiding the telescope on the Sun to the accuracy required even for the very short exposure times involved in direct photography (in this case about 1·5 milliseconds). In addition, mechanical vibrations in the servo guiding system were a major source of difficulty, despite determined attempts to eliminate them. In fact, even on the best flights only about 5 per cent of the photographs showed the theoretical performance of the telescope.

Nevertheless, despite these difficulties Project Stratoscope I did serve to demonstrate the essential feasibility of making solar observations from a balloon-borne telescope. Moreover, it directly stimulated astronomers at the Fraunhofer Institut in Germany to embark upon an even more ambitious undertaking, namely to obtain spectra of selected solar features together with simultaneous photographs taken either in white light or Hα. This new venture, which has been appropriately named Project Spectro-Stratoscope, is described in the following section.

5.4.2 PROJECT SPECTRO-STRATOSCOPE

Figure 5.7 shows the optical system of the new telescope and spectrograph which are being constructed for Project Spectro-Stratoscope by the firm of Carl Zeiss at Oberkochen, West Germany [Kiepenheuer and Mehltretter, 1964]. The general layout is based on the design of the telescope used in Project Stratoscope I and incorporates the same 12-inch objective mirror *M*. This mirror, which is made of fused quartz and has a focal length of 8 ft, forms a primary image of the Sun at a point P_1. Light from a small selected region of the primary image (about 2′ of arc square) is then diverted sideways by a small Newtonian mirror and re-imaged on the entrance slit *S* of a Littrow-type spectrograph with the aid of a magnifying lens L_1. The spectrograph is equipped with a Bausch and Lomb diffraction grating *G* ruled with 600 lines/mm over an area of 16×21 cm^2; it will be used in the fourth order

[11] For full information on the design and operation of Stratoscope I the reader is referred to the following sources: Rogerson [1958]; Schwarzschild [1959]; Schwarzschild and Schwarzschild [1959]; Danielson [1961]; Bray and Loughhead [1964: p. 32].

for the red (in the neighbourhood of Hα) and in the fifth order for the green, the resolving power being about 400,000. A small part of the primary spectrum produced by the spectrograph at P_2 is magnified and projected onto the gate of a 70-mm camera C_1. The dispersion in the final image plane will be about 10 mm/Å, while the angular scale of the image in the direction at right angles to the dispersion will be 3″.3 of arc/mm.

The entrance slit S of the spectrograph is made by ruling a fine line in an aluminium coating deposited on a polished quartz plate. The image formed on this plate is reflected, magnified, and projected onto the gate of a second camera C_2. Preceding C_2 there is a 0·5Å birefringent filter F, designed to isolate Hα, and a beam-splitter B, which produces an auxiliary white-light

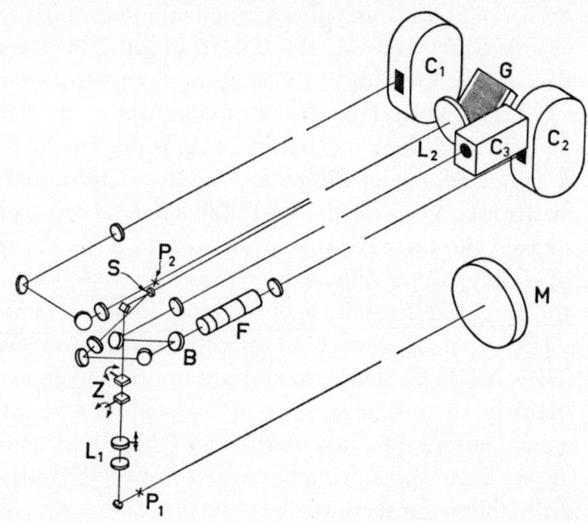

Fig. 5.7. Spectro-Stratoscope: optical layout [Kiepenheuer and Mehltretter, 1964]. M, objective mirror; P_1, position of prime focus; L_1, magnifying lens; S, entrance slit of spectrograph; L_2, collimating lens; G, diffraction grating; P_2, position of primary spectrum; C_1, C_2, cameras; C_3, TV camera; B, beam splitter; F, Hα birefringent filter; Z, guiding plates. The mechanical framework of the instrument is shown in Fig. 5.8.

image on a TV camera C_3. This image is transmitted to the observers on the ground and is also used for the fine guiding system described below. Means are provided for varying the exposure times of the two cameras C_1 and C_2 separately over the range 1–20 sec, to alter the time sequences of exposures, to shift the transmission band of the Hα filter, and to change the region of the spectrum being photographed by ±10Å. On both the white-light and Hα images the spectrograph slit appears as a dark line across the field of view, thus enabling the location of the slit with respect to the image to be ascertained accurately for each spectrum.

Due to temperature changes, relatively large variations in the position of best focus must be expected during the flights. To overcome this difficulty, an automatic device for focusing the image is provided: a tiny hole is used to scan the photospheric granulation pattern and so generate a signal whose magnitude is proportional to the sharpness of the image. The magnifying lens L_1 is then moved to the position where the maximum response is obtained. In passing, we may remark that, in view of the large number of auxiliary mirrors and lenses present in the image-forming systems (see Fig. 5.7), each component needs to be manufactured with unusual precision if the full theoretical performance of the telescope is to be achieved.

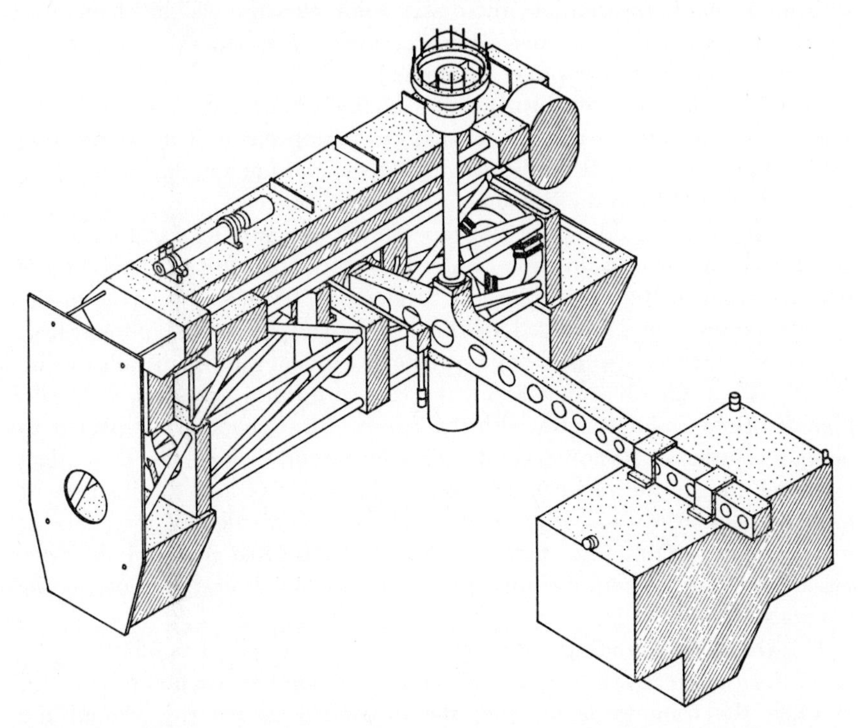

Fig. 5.8. Spectro-Stratoscope: mechanical assembly [Kiepenheuer and Mehltretter, 1964]. The instrument framework is supported by a spherical oil-pressure bearing which permits rotation about three mutually perpendicular axes. A box containing electrical batteries and other auxiliary equipment is mounted on the end of a long arm to act as a counter-weight. Three crash-pads are attached, one beneath the box and two beneath the framework. The small telescope mounted on top of the framework forms part of the guidance system.

As illustrated in Fig. 5.8, the telescope, spectrograph, and cameras are all mounted within a compact mechanical framework. This is supported at its centre of gravity by a spherical oil-pressure bearing which, in turn, is carried by the main supporting structure; it is located at the left-hand end of the horizontal beam shown in Fig. 5.8, but is not itself visible in the illustration. The spherical bearing is surrounded by a concentric assembly of three torque motors which provide a means of controlling the orientation of the framework around three mutually perpendicular axes. A box containing electrical batteries and parts of the remote control system is mounted on the other end of the horizontal beam to act as a counter-weight to the instrument framework. Three crash-pads are mounted below the combined structure, one beneath the box and two beneath the framework. This design places the overall centre of gravity in a relatively low position and hence decreases the chance of the instrument's overturning and being damaged on impact with the ground. In addition, the design minimizes the weight of the supporting structure and provides a high azimuthal inertia against which the orientation control torques may be applied.

In order to de-couple the instrument from the balloon suspension assembly, a second oil-pressure bearing is inserted at the upper end of the supporting frame. A torque motor at this bearing enables azimuthal angular momentum to be transferred from the instrument to the balloon.

The problem of guiding the telescope on the Sun is crucial to the success of Project Spectro-Stratoscope. Indeed, very much greater stability is required than in the case of Project Stratoscope I where, by virtue of the short exposure times involved in direct photography of the photosphere (about 1 millisecond), some swinging of the instrument was permissible during the exposures. On the other hand, the exposure times necessary to obtain high-dispersion solar spectra with the Spectro-Stratoscope are expected to be of the order of several seconds. This means that, since the theoretical resolving limit of the 12-inch objective is about $0''.4$ of arc, the instrument must be held steady to within a small fraction of this figure for periods of some seconds at a time. To meet this requirement, the firm of Zeiss is developing a three-stage system designed to provide a guiding accuracy of $0''.1$ for intervals of up to 30 sec.

This three-stage guiding system may be briefly described as follows:

(1) *Acquisition and coarse guiding.* When the balloon has reached the desired altitude, the framework carrying the instrument is rotated around the vertical axis to the correct azimuthal angle by a simple servo system controlling the torque motor located at the upper oil-pressure bearing mentioned above. This system continues to function until the time of descent, stabilizing the whole gondola in azimuth to about 1°. Once this condition is achieved, a similar servo is used to tilt the telescope framework to the correct elevation angle; the instrument is then clamped in this position and the next stage of the guiding system switched on. The necessary guiding signals for the two coarse servo systems are provided by pairs of ordinary photodiodes.

(2) *Intermediate guiding.* This is achieved by a conventional photoelectric guider detecting displacements of the limb on an auxiliary solar image formed by a small telescope mounted on top of the instrument framework (see Fig. 5.8). The error signals from the guider actuate two of the three torque motors around the main spherical telescope bearing. In this way it is

hoped to keep the guider telescope pointed at the centre of the Sun to an accuracy of better than 1″ of arc. The angle between the guider and the main telescope can be changed by command from the ground, thus enabling any chosen region of the Sun to be brought onto the spectrograph slit.

(3) *Fine guiding.* The final step in attaining the required guiding accuracy is accomplished by the use of two plane-parallel quartz plates (labelled Z in Fig. 5.7) located in the light beam between the magnifying lens L_1 and the spectrograph slit S. These plates rotate about two axes at right angles to the optical axis and are servo-controlled to keep the image stationary on S to about 0″.1. The necessary error signals are obtained by means of an ingenious photoelectric device located in one corner of the auxiliary white-light image furnished by the beam splitter B (see above). A tetrahedral prism is placed behind a small aperture which is just large enough to accommodate one photospheric granule, and the light from the four quadrants of the granule is allowed to fall on four photomultipliers. Any inequality in a given pair of output signals is then fed back to the corresponding moving plate.

However, this device does not prevent rotation of the image about a line through the apex of the tetrahedral prism. To stop this, a similar granulation sensor is provided at the opposite corner of the white-light image. It consists of a small aperture in the shape of a half disk and provides an error signal which is fed to the torque motor controlling roll about the main telescope bearing.

Owing to differences in the shape, size, and brightness of individual granules and to their limited lifetimes (Section 2.2), the fine guider naturally works on a somewhat statistical basis. However, by using granulation photographs obtained with Stratoscope I the engineers at Zeiss have been able to simulate the operation of the fine guiding system in the laboratory and carefully study its performance. The results indicate that excellent guiding over intervals of up to 30 sec is to be expected in 50 per cent or more of cases. Moreover, recent work has suggested that it may be possible to achieve a guiding accuracy of 0″.1 by means of the *intermediate* guider alone. This would in any case be necessary for observations near the solar limb, where the granulation guider obviously cannot be used.

The actual flights of Project Spectro-Stratoscope will be undertaken in the United States in collaboration with the National Center for Atmospheric Research at Boulder, Colorado, and are scheduled to begin in 1966. If fully successful, they may well usher in a new era of spectroscopy both of the photospheric granulation and of the Sun's fine structure as a whole.

5.4.3 SATELLITE-BORNE TELESCOPES AND SPACE PROBES

Despite the valuable contributions to the study of the Sun's fine structure which may be expected to result from the development of balloon-borne instruments such as Spectro-Stratoscope, there seems little doubt that ultimately they will be superseded by satellite-borne telescopes capable of making systematic observations with a resolution of 0″.1 of arc or better. On the other hand, it must be admitted that the best resolution which has so far been achieved in solar observations from satellites does not exceed about 1′ of arc. The basic reason for this lies in the difficulty of stabilizing and guiding a satellite-borne telescope with the necessary high accuracy. However, as we have already seen, precisely the same problem has to be faced in the case of balloon-borne instruments, and the experience gained from Project Spectro-Stratoscope and any similar future undertakings will therefore be vital to the development of more refined satellite techniques.

On March 7, 1962, the United States National Aeronautics and Space Administration (N.A.S.A.) launched the first of a series of Orbiting Solar Observatories (O.S.O.) which are intended to make measurements of the Sun's radiation in the ultraviolet, X-ray, and γ-ray regions of the spectrum throughout the course of a solar cycle [see, for example, *Sky and Telescope* **23,** 256; LeGalley, 1964: p. 24]. The objectives also include observations of solar flares, plage activity, and prominences, as well as the measurement of high-energy particles above the Earth's atmosphere. On the other hand, the O.S.O. is not designed to achieve any high degree of spatial resolution, although provision is made for mounting instruments on a small stabilized platform which is kept directed towards the Sun with an accuracy of 1–2′ of arc. However, work is already proceeding on the design of a series of Advanced Orbiting Solar Observatories (A.O.S.O.) which should enable observations to be made with a resolution approaching a few seconds of arc [cf. LeGalley, 1964: p. 25].

Moreover, N.A.S.A.'s plans to improve the spatial resolution attained in satellite observations do not stop with the A.O.S.O. series. In a private communication, H. J. Smith comments as follows on the likely course of events over the next decade or so:

> 'As I see it, we shall use O.S.O. and sounding rockets over the remainder of this decade, to achieve one arc minute pointing and telescopic resolution. By 1970 we shall begin to use the Advanced O.S.O., with about 5 arc seconds pointing and resolution capability. At the same time we shall probably begin using A.O.S.O. size telescopes (4- to 12-inch aperture) on manned spacecraft, but probably with no better than one-half arc minute stabilization. Whether "instantaneous photography" will permit such instruments to attain higher effective resolution, only time will tell. I hopefully expect this will be achieved. Approximately ten years hence, astronauts may carry an A.O.S.O. into orbit, operate it in a tethered (i.e., dynamically de-coupled) mode to secure high rate photographic observations for short (10–30 day) missions, perhaps with slightly improved resolution. However, we know that the servo-guiders of A.O.S.O. will be limited by thermal noise and by digital resolver scale size, to about 2 arc seconds. It is possible that second level guidance might permit up to an order of magnitude improvement (say $\frac{1}{4}$ arc second, with a 20-inch

telescope) on this system. Supporting experience won't be available for five years at the earliest.'

According to Smith it may take two decades for satellite techniques to develop to the point where the attainment of $0''.1$ of arc resolution becomes possible.[12]

The development of a highly stabilized satellite for solar observations has also been proposed recently as a possible long-term goal of the European Space Research Organization (E.S.R.O.), which was set up in 1964 to promote collaboration in space research and technology among the European nations [Lüst, 1965]. At the moment E.S.R.O. has a membership of ten: Belgium, Denmark, France, Germany, Italy, the Netherlands, Spain, Sweden, Switzerland, and the United Kingdom. Initially, one of E.S.R.O.'s major projects will be the development of a large astronomical satellite designed primarily to obtain spectra of stars over the range 900–3000Å with a spectral resolution of 1Å or better. It is likely that several such satellites may ultimately be launched, and the experience so gained would be of great value in the subsequent development of a highly stabilized satellite for high-resolution solar observations.

No information is known to the authors about any possible plans which the Soviet Union may have to develop a highly stabilized satellite of its own. However, this country has repeatedly demonstrated its ability to launch satellites of exceptional weight, recently as much as 12 tons (12,200 kg). Such a satellite should certainly be capable of carrying a large solar telescope, together with a compact spectrograph and other auxiliary equipment.

One final perspective in the development of extra-terrestrial observing techniques is the exciting possibility of one day sending a space probe to the immediate vicinity of the Sun [cf. Goldberg and Dyer, 1961: p. 336]. Such a proposal has much to commend it: a solar probe would enable photographic and spectroscopic observations of the Sun's fine structure to be obtained with unprecedented spatial resolution with a telescope of modest size. A striking illustration of the great potentialities of space probes has recently been provided by the brilliant success of the N.A.S.A. probe, *Mariner 4*, in obtaining close-up pictures of the planet Mars and transmitting them back over a distance of some 135,000,000 miles [see, for example, Watts, 1965; Leighton, Murray, Sharp, Allen, and Sloan, 1965]. By comparison, the mean Earth–Sun distance is about 93,000,000 miles. However, the practical realization of a solar probe would encounter formidable technical difficulties. Foremost among these is the problem of coping with the high radiant temperatures in the neighbourhood of the Sun. As Goldberg and Dyer point out, at a distance of four solar radii the radiant temperature is about 3000°K, which is roughly the melting point of the most refractory substances known and certainly far above the working limit of present-day

[12] Dr Smith is Chief of the N.A.S.A. Solar Physics Program. We are greatly indebted to him for the remarks quoted above.

probes. Secondly, there is the difficulty of transmitting radio signals through the tenuous ionized gases surrounding the Sun and, in addition, of overcoming the interference likely to be caused by ejected clouds of solar plasma. Finally, there is the problem of the possible harmful effect of high energy particles on the solar cells supplying electrical power and on the electronic and other delicate instrumentation.

REFERENCES

BRAY, R. J., and LOUGHHEAD, R. E. [1961] 'Facular granule lifetimes determined with a seeing-monitored photoheliograph', *Aust. J. Phys.* **14,** 14.

BRAY, R. J., and LOUGHHEAD, R. E. [1964] *Sunspots.* (Chapman and Hall: London).

BRAY, R. J., LOUGHHEAD, R. E., and NORTON, D. G. [1959] 'A "seeing monitor" to aid solar observation', *Observatory* **79,** 63.

DANIELSON, R. E. [1961] 'The structure of sunspot penumbras. I. Observations', *Astrophys. J.* **134,** 275.

EVANS, J. W. [1964] 'Solar magnetographs'. (*Atti Convegno Sui Campi Magnetici Solari, Rome, 1964,* p. 23; Rome).

GOLDBERG, L., and DYER, E. R. [1961] 'The Sun'. (*Science in Space,* eds. L. V. BERKNER and H. ODISHAW, p. 307; McGraw-Hill: New York).

KIEPENHEUER, K. O. [1963] 'Solar site testing'. (I.A.U. Symposium No. 19: 'Le Choix des Sites d'Observatoires Astronomiques', *Bull. Astron. Obs. Paris* **24**(2,3), 193).

KIEPENHEUER, K. O. [1964] 'A domeless coudé refractor for solar work', *Appl. Optics* **3,** 1363.

KIEPENHEUER, K. O., and MEHLTRETTER, J. P. [1964] 'Spectrostratoscope: a balloon-borne solar observatory', *Appl. Optics* **3,** 1359.

KUPREVICH, N. F. [1964] 'On some photoelectric and television methods of elimination of atmospheric turbulence effects during astronomical observations', *Izv. Pulkovo Astron. Obs.* **23**(5), 144.

LEGALLEY, D. P. [1964] 'Introduction – programs for the conquest of space'. (*Space Physics,* eds. D. P. LEGALLEY and A. ROSEN, p. 1; John Wiley: New York).

LEIGHTON, R. B., MURRAY, B. C., SHARP, R. P., ALLEN, J. D., and SLOAN, R. K. [1965] 'Mariner IV photography of Mars: initial results', *Science* **149,** 627.

LOUGHHEAD, R. E., and BRAY, R. J. [1966] 'Statistics of solar seeing', *Z. Astrophys.* **63,** 101.

LUMLEY, J. L., and PANOFSKY, H. A. [1964] *The Structure of Atmospheric Turbulence.* (Interscience: New York).

LÜST, R. [1965] 'The European Space Research Organization', *Science* **149,** 394.

MCMATH, R. R., and MOHLER, O. C. [1962] 'Solar instruments'. (*Handbuch der Physik*, ed S. FLÜGGE, vol. 54, p. 1; Springer: Berlin).

PRIESTLEY, C. H. B. [1959] *Turbulent Transfer in the Lower Atmosphere*. (Univ. Chicago Press).

ROGERSON, J. B. [1958] 'Project Stratoscope', *Sky and Tel.* **17**, 112.

SCHWARZSCHILD, M. [1959] 'Photographs of the solar granulation taken from the stratosphere', *Astrophys. J.* **130**, 345.

SCHWARZSCHILD, M., and SCHWARZSCHILD, B. [1959] 'Balloon astronomy', *Sci. Amer.* **200**(5), 52.

SIEDENTOPF, H., and UNZ, F. [1964] 'Temperature fluctuations in the atmospheric ground layer observed at Zeekoegat and Flathill (South Africa)'. (European South. Obs. Publ.: Astron. Inst. Univ. Tübingen).

TATARSKII, V. I. [1956] 'The microstructure of the temperature field in the layer of atmosphere near the ground', *Izv. Acad. Nauk U.S.S.R., Geophys. Ser.*, No. 6, 689.

VUL'FSON, N. I. [1964] *Convective Motions in a Free Atmosphere*. (Israel Program for Scientific Translations: Jerusalem).

WATTS, R. N. [1965] 'Mariner 4 completes Mars mission', *Sky and Tel.* **30**, 136.

WEBB, E. K. [1964] 'Daytime thermal fluctuations in the lower atmosphere', *Appl. Optics* **3**, 1329.

ZINDEL, D. [1963] 'Ein Gerät zur lichtelektrischen Bildschärfemessung', *Z. Astrophys.* **57**, 83.

INDEXES

Name Index

Subject Index

(*Note:* unless otherwise apparent, entries refer to the *photospheric granulation.*)